# Verbal Reasoning

## Assessment Papers

## 10–11+ years

## Book 2

Great Clarendon Street, Oxford, OX2 6DP, United Kingdom

Oxford University Press is a department of the University of Oxford. It furthers the University's objective of excellence in research, scholarship, and education by publishing worldwide. Oxford is a registered trade mark of Oxford University Press in the UK and in certain other countries



First published in 2015



British Library Cataloguing in Publication Data
Data available

978-0-19-274036-6

10 9 8 7 6 5 4 3

Paper used in the production of this book is a natural, recyclable product made from wood grown in sustainable forests.
The manufacturing process conforms to the environmental regulations of the country of origin.

Printed in China

**Acknowledgements**

The publishers would like to thank the following for permissions to use copyright material:

Page make-up: OKS Prepress, India
Cover illustrations: Lo Cole

Although we have made every effort to trace and contact all copyright holders before publication this has not been possible in all cases. If notified, the publisher will rectify any errors or omissions at the earliest opportunity.

# Before you get started

## What is Bond?

This book is part of the Bond Assessment Papers series for verbal reasoning, which provides a **thorough and progressive course in verbal reasoning** from ages six to twelve. It builds up verbal reasoning skills from book to book over the course of the series.

Bond's verbal reasoning resources are ideal preparation for the 11⁺ and other secondary school selection exams.

## How does the scope of this book match real exam content?

*Verbal Reasoning 10–11⁺ Book 1* and *Book 2* are the core Bond 11⁺ books. Each paper is **pitched at the level of a typical 11⁺ exam** and practises a wide range of questions drawn from the four distinct groups of verbal reasoning question types: sorting words, selecting words, anagrams, coded sequences and logic. The papers are fully in line with 11⁺ and other selective exams for this age group but are designed to practise **a wider variety of skills and question types** than most other practice papers so that children are always challenged to think – and don't get bored repeating the same question type again and again. We believe that variety is the key to effective learning. It helps children 'think on their feet' and cope with the unexpected: it is surprising how often children come out of verbal reasoning exams having met question types they have not seen before.

## What does the book contain?

- **13 papers** – each one contains 80 questions.
- **Tutorial links throughout** – 📖 – this icon appears in the margin next to the questions. It indicates links to the relevant section in *How to do 11⁺ Verbal Reasoning*, our invaluable subject guide that offers explanations and practice for all core question types.
- **Scoring devices** – there are score boxes in the margins and a Progress Chart on page 60. The chart is a visual and motivating way for children to see how they are doing. It also turns the score into a percentage that can help you decide what to do next.
- **Next Steps Planner** – advice on what to do after finishing the papers can be found on the inside back cover.
- **Answers** – located in an easily-removed central pull-out section.

## How can you use this book?

One of the great strengths of Bond Assessment Papers is their flexibility. They can be used at home, in school and by tutors to:

- set **timed formal practice tests** – allow about 45 minutes per paper in line with standard 11⁺ demands. Reduce the suggested time limit by five minutes to practise working at speed.

- provide **bite-sized chunks** for regular practice
- **highlight strengths and weaknesses** in the core skills
- identify **individual needs**
- set **homework**
- follow **a complete 11⁺ preparation strategy** alongside *The Parents' Guide to the 11⁺* (see below).

It is best to start at the beginning and work through the papers in order. If you are using the book as part of a careful run-in to the 11⁺, we suggest that you also have two other essential Bond resources close at hand:

*How to do 11⁺ Verbal Reasoning*: the subject guide that explains all the question types practised in this book. Use the cross-reference icons to find the relevant sections.

*The Parents' Guide to the 11⁺*: the step-by-step guide to the whole 11⁺ experience. It clearly explains the 11⁺ process, provides guidance on how to assess children, helps you to set complete action plans for practice and explains how you can use *Verbal Reasoning 10–11⁺ Book 1* and *Book 2* as part of a strategic run-in to the exam.

See the inside front cover for more details of these books.

## What does a child's score mean and how can it be improved?

It is unfortunately impossible to guarantee that a child will pass the 11⁺ exam if they achieve a certain score on any practice book or paper. Success on the day depends on a host of factors, including the scores of the other children sitting the test. However, we can give some guidance on what a score indicates and how to improve it.

If children colour in the Progress Chart on page 60, this will give an idea of present performance in percentage terms. The Next Steps Planner inside the back cover will help you to decide what to do next to help a child progress. It is always valuable to go over wrong answers with children. If they are having trouble with any particular question type, follow the tutorial links to *How to do 11⁺ Verbal Reasoning* for step-by-step explanations and further practice.

## *Don't forget the website...!*

Visit www.bond11plus.co.uk for lots of advice, information and suggestions on everything to do with Bond, the 11⁺ and helping children to do their best.

# Paper 1

Find and underline the two words which need to change places for each sentence to make sense. B 17

**Example** She went to <u>letter</u> the <u>write</u>.

1 The queue to the museum stood in the visitors.

2 Not had she packed any lunch.

3 Most bones like dogs.

4 I ran upstairs get to my book.

5 Out jumped he of the tree. 5

Underline one word in the brackets which is most opposite in meaning to the word in capitals. B 6

**Example** WIDE (broad vague long <u>narrow</u> motorway)

6 APPEAR (look image vanish seem arrival)

7 SILENT (quiet shy peaceful noisy still)

8 RISE (grow descend slope raise position)

9 PLAIN (flat fancy simple ugly clear)

10 RUNNY (flowing solid stream dashing liquid) 5

**11–15** Look at these groups of words. B 1

| A | B | C | D |
|---|---|---|---|
| hamster | peach | tennis | cod |
| elephant | plum | cricket | haddock |

Choose the correct group for each of the words below. Write in the letter.

trout ___ kiwi ___ rounders ___ cheetah ___ plaice ___

satsuma ___ weasel ___ salmon ___ lacrosse ___ badminton ___ 5

Underline two words, one from each group, that go together to form a new word. The word in the first group always comes first. B 8

**Example** (hand, <u>green</u>, for) (light, <u>house</u>, sure)

16 (moth, ant, frog) (hop, eater, tick)

17 (bottom, lap, write) (pencil, ink, top)

18 (more, make, need) (want, less, done)

19 (friend, sea, wreck) (best, kind, ship)

20 (fox, skip, broad) (den, cast, rope) 5

Underline the pair of words most similar in meaning.

**Example** come, go <u>roam, wander</u> fear, fare

21 night, dawn seldom, often guess, suspect

22 hand, foot option, choice few, many

23 diminish, lessen proceed, stop absence, presence

24 near, far ruler, controller need, wish

25 dog, pet solid, hollow job, task

Aiden and Chloe like tennis.
Beth and Chloe like football, but not swimming.
Only Daxa likes tennis and swimming.

26 Which sport is most popular? ______________

If A = 2, B = 4, C = 5 and D = 6, give the answers to each of these calculations as a letter.

27 (D − B) × A = ___

28 D + B − C = ___

29 (A × B) ÷ B = ___

Fill in the crosswords so that all the given words are included. You have been given one letter as a clue in each crossword.

**30–31**

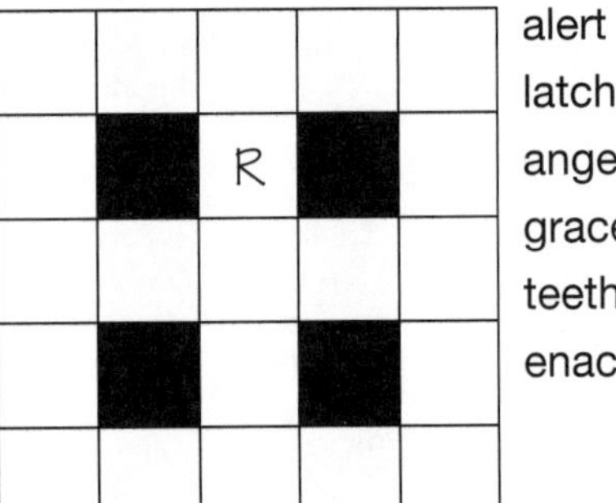


alert
latch
angel
grace
teeth
enact

**32–33**

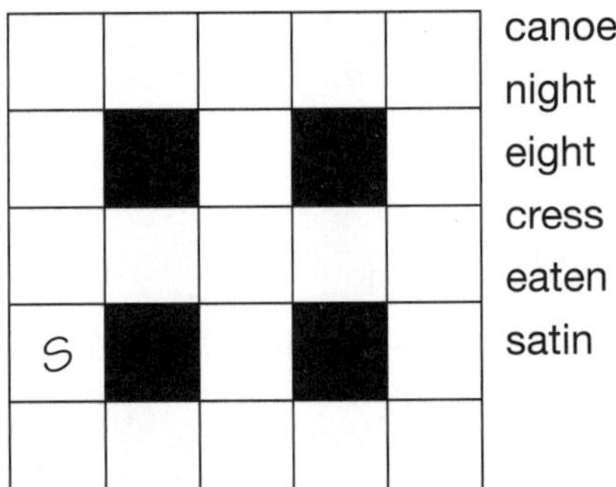


canoe
night
eight
cress
eaten
satin

Fill in the missing letters. The alphabet has been written out to help you.

A B C D E F G H I J K L M N O P Q R S T U V W X Y Z

**Example** AB is to CD as PQ is to <u>RS</u>.

34 CD is to EF as IJ is to ______.

35 FH is to HG as MO is to ______.

36 XV is to UY as JH is to ______.

37 RN is to SO as BD is to ______.

38 AD is to ZW as CF is to ______.

If * ^ % £ ! ^ ~ # is the code for H O M E W O R K, what are the codes for these words? B 24

39 MORE ____________

40 WORM ____________

41 MEEK ____________

42 WHERE ____________

43 ROOM ____________

5

Laura, Omar, James, Kate, Eva and Jacob are six children. Omar is older than Kate, but younger than Laura. James is the oldest child and Eva is not the youngest. Kate is older than just two children. B 25

List the children in order of age, starting with the oldest.

44 ____________

45 ____________

46 ____________

47 ____________

48 ____________

49 ____________

6

Give the two missing numbers in the following sequences. B 23

| | | | | | | |
|---|---|---|---|---|---|---|
| **Example** | 2 | 4 | 6 | 8 | 10 | 12 |
| **50** 16 | 13 | 17 | ___ | ___ | 15 | |
| **51** 3 | 6 | 12 | ___ | ___ | 96 | |
| **52** 2 | 3 | 5 | ___ | 8 | ___ | |
| **53** 7 | ___ | 12 | 16 | 21 | ___ | |
| **54** 5 | 1 | 10 | ___ | ___ | 3 | |

5

Find the letter which will end the first word and start the second word. B 10

**Example** peac (h) ome

55 pos (___) rip

56 wor (___) oan

57 war (___) haw

58 lic (___) ase

59 her (___) amp

5

Change the first word into the last word, by changing one letter at a time and making a new, different word in the middle. B 13

**Example** CASE CASH LASH

60 STOP ______ STEM

61 LOVE ______ GIVE

62 JEER ______ DEAR

63 BAIT ______ PAIL

64 CRAB ______ GRUB 5

Underline the one word in the brackets which will go equally well with both the pairs of words outside the brackets. B 5

**Example** rush, attack cost, fee (price, hasten, strike, charge, money)

65 regarding, concerning roughly, nearly (refer, close, about, almost, talking)

66 unlocked, unfastened start, launch (gaping, place, open, shut, begin)

67 break, crack bite, nip (quick, snap, twig, burst, sharp)

68 faded, dim collapse, black out (dizzy, light, sick, faint, dull)

69 annoyed, grumpy circle, square (shape, angry, cross, diamond, cut) 5

Read the first two statements and then underline one of the four options below that must be true. B 25

70 'Chairs are furniture. Furniture can be made of wood.'

Trees supply wood.

Wood is used for all furniture.

Chairs can be made of wood.

Trees are furniture because they are wood. 1

Find the four-letter word hidden at the end of one word and the beginning of the next word. The order of the letters may not be changed. B 21

**Example** The children had bats and balls. sand

71 If you blow and blow the candle will go out. ______

72 The argument began when Laurie took Jenna's phone. ______

73 Each opponent must weigh in first. ______

74 Will you help me find one that isn't broken. ______

75 The rabbits stayed quite still as we passed. ______ 5

Underline the one word which **cannot be made** from the letters of the word in capital letters. B 7

| | | | | | | |
|---|---|---|---|---|---|---|
| **Example** | STATIONERY | stone | tyres | ration | <u>nation</u> | noisy |
| **76** | DIGESTION | signet | onset | notice | tides | stone |
| **77** | INTENSIVE | tense | sieve | veins | events | nineteen |
| **78** | UNDERNEATH | tender | earth | turned | dated | heated |
| **79** | THURSDAY | shard | dusty | thuds | rusty | hurry |
| **80** | ANSWERED | swear | drawer | snared | swede | waned |

5

***Now go to the Progress Chart to record your score!*** Total 80

# Paper 2

Give the two missing numbers in the following sequences. B 23

| | | | | | | |
|---|---|---|---|---|---|---|
| **Example** | 2 | 4 | 6 | 8 | <u>10</u> | <u>12</u> |
| **1** | 63 | ___ | 49 | 42 | 35 | ___ |
| **2** | 4 | 8 | ___ | 32 | 64 | ___ |
| **3** | 19 | ___ | 15 | ___ | 11 | 9 |
| **4** | 12 | 14 | ___ | 19 | 22 | ___ |
| **5** | 27 | 24 | 23 | ___ | 19 | ___ |

5

In 3 years' time Sarah will be twice as old as Emma was last year. Emma is now 11. B 25

**6** How old is Sarah now? ________ 1

Here are the number codes for four words. Match the right word to the right code. B 24

| WALL | LAMP | MALE | PALE |
|---|---|---|---|
| 5274 | 3255 | 4256 | 7256 |

**7** WALL ________

**8** LAMP ________

**9** MALE ________

**10** PALE ________

**11** Write the code for LEAP. ________ 5

Complete the following sentences in the best way by choosing one word from each set of brackets.

**Example** Tall is to (tree, short, colour) as narrow is to (thin, white, wide).

**12** Horse is to (foal, stable, saddle) as cow is to (milk, grass, calf).

**13** Car is to (petrol, speed, driver) as aeroplane is to (pilot, holiday, airport).

**14** Hurry is to (hasten, slow, move) as assemble is to (school, repeat, gather).

**15** Match is to (burn, stick, game) as head is to (hair, body, boss).

**16** Spring is to (summer, season, jump) as march is to (calendar, walk, winter).

Rearrange the muddled letters in capitals to make a proper word. The answer will complete the sentence sensibly.

**Example** A BEZAR is an animal with stripes. ZEBRA

**17** Look right and left before you SORCS the road. ______

**18** Katie enjoyed her summer YHLADOI. ______

**19** He used the LERUR to underline the title. ______

**20** She hurt her STRIW. ______

**21** The whole class went to the YAPTR. ______

Underline the one word in the brackets which will go equally well with both the pairs of words outside the brackets.

| | | | |
|---|---|---|---|
| **Example** | rush, attack | cost, fee | (price, hasten, strike, charge, money) |
| **22** | end, point | empty, pour out | (nib, spill, tip, rubbish, top) |
| **23** | bounce, leap | leave out, miss | (jump, try, ball, skip, forget) |
| **24** | guide, teach | performance, act | (parade, explain, show, amuse, lead) |
| **25** | location, area | arrange, put | (spot, flowers, live, place, keep) |
| **26** | document, folder | note, store | (notice, paper, file, remark, keep) |

Find the missing number by using the two numbers outside the brackets in the same way as the other sets of numbers.

| | | | |
|---|---|---|---|
| **Example** | 2 [8] 4 | 3 [18] 6 | 5 [25] 5 |
| **27** | 5 [15] 10 | 7 [15] 8 | 3 [___] 13 |
| **28** | 6 [2] 4 | 15 [10] 5 | 12 [___] 8 |
| **29** | 12 [24] 2 | 9 [27] 3 | 8 [___] 5 |
| **30** | 6 [12] 5 | 4 [8] 3 | 12 [___] 2 |
| **31** | 13 [16] 3 | 12 [23] 11 | 8 [___] 17 |

Complete the following sentences by selecting the most sensible word from each group of words given in the brackets. Underline the words selected. B 14

**Example** The (children, books, foxes) carried the (houses, books, steps) home from the (greengrocer, library, factory).

**32** The (girl, puppy, toy) asked her (toy, mother, bone) for some (rain, shops, sweets).

**33** Remember to (cross, ask, check) your (work, friend, breakfast) before handing it to the (dentist, teacher, waiter).

**34** They enjoy (skipping, riding, swimming) their (horses, boats, fish) in the (playground, field, pitch).

**35** Mix the (bowl, butter, kitchen) with the (sugar, mustard, medicine), then add some (detergent, powder, eggs).

**36** The weather was (foggy, sunny, frosty) and too (easy, moody, hot) to play on the (beach, circus, cinema). 5

Underline two words, one from each group, that go together to form a new word. The word in the first group always comes first. B 8

**Example** (hand, green, for) (light, house, sure)

**37** (small, cross, draw) (shout, shape, roads)

**38** (share, cap, telephone) (size, cause, ring)

**39** (use, beauty, me) (full, less, all)

**40** (grass, sea, shine) (sun, bright, weed)

**41** (go, near, walk) (close, far, by) 5

Move one letter from the first word and add it to the second word to make two new words. B 13

**Example** hunt sip hut snip

**42** climb rack ______ ______

**43** forty part ______ ______

**44** splay crumb ______ ______

**45** ruin deal ______ ______

**46** thrust sore ______ ______ 5

Underline the two words, one from each group, which are closest in meaning. B 3

**Example** (race, shop, start) (finish, begin, end)

**47** (calm, sea, cool) (wind, still, waves)

**48** (sun, beam, star) (hot, shine, sky)

**49** (dog, scratch, claw) (graze, knee, sore)

**50** (fair, rich, dark) (poor, honest, reliable)

**51** (hit, fall, force) (hand, power, fail) 5

Find the letter which will end the first word and start the second word.

**Example** peac ( h ) ome

52 note ( __ ) eaf

53 jump ( __ ) hape

54 rai ( __ ) aft

55 kne ( __ ) ide

56 fro ( __ ) lee

B 10 5

Find the three-letter word which can be added to the letters in capitals to make a new word. The new word will complete the sentence sensibly.

**Example** The cat sprang onto the MO. USE

57 He ate fish and CS in the café. ______

58 The NOT appeared in the newspaper. ______

59 I helped my mother with the SPING. ______

60 Try to LN your spellings in time for the test. ______

61 The car SPED at the traffic lights. ______

B 22 5

Fill in the crosswords so that all the given words are included. You have been given one letter as a clue in each crossword.

62–63

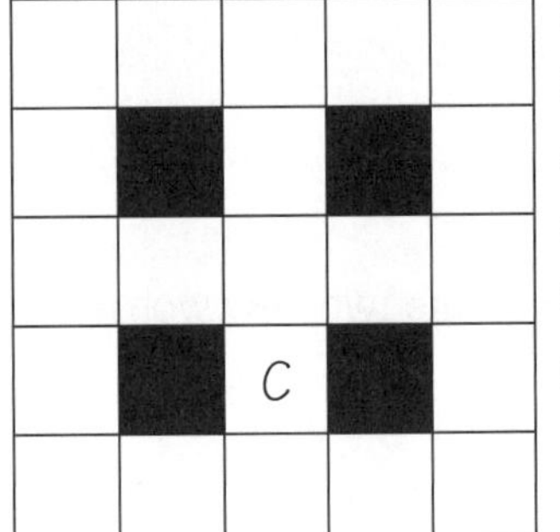


aloft
agree
ounce
exert
treat
rinse

64–65

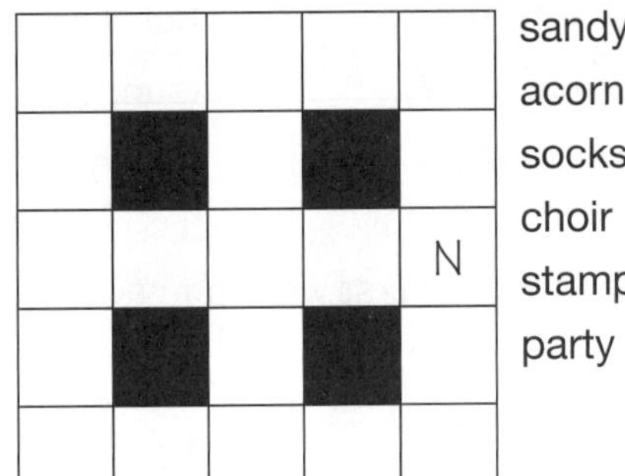


sandy
acorn
socks
choir
stamp
party

B 19 4

Give the two missing groups of letters in the following sequences. The alphabet has been written out to help you.

A B C D E F G H I J K L M N O P Q R S T U V W X Y Z

| | | | | | | |
|---|---|---|---|---|---|---|
| **Example** | CQ | DP | EQ | FP | GQ | HP |
| 66 | ZA | ______ | XC | WD | ______ | UF |
| 67 | CA | EC | GE | IG | ______ | ______ |
| 68 | VAJ | WBK | XCL | YDM | ______ | ______ |
| 69 | AT | DR | ______ | JN | ______ | PJ |
| 70 | PA | BQ | RC | DS | ______ | ______ |

B 23 5

If P = 6, Q = 4, R = 2, S = 12 and T = 8, give the answer to each of these calculations as a letter.

**71** $P + Q + R =$ ___ 　 **72** $(Q \times Q) - (P - R) =$ ___

**73** $Q \times R =$ ___ 　 **74** $S \div R =$ ___

**75** $(R \times T) \div Q =$ ___

Which one letter can be added to the front of all of these words to make new words?

| **Example** | <u>c</u>are | <u>c</u>at | <u>c</u>rate | <u>c</u>all |
|---|---|---|---|---|
| **76** ___owl | ___one | ___reak | ___ray | ___rain |
| **77** ___am | ___oint | ___ump | ___ust | ___ewel |
| **78** ___ront | ___oil | ___lower | ___orce | ___ool |
| **79** ___ake | ___ait | ___eed | ___ild | ___hat |
| **80** ___ear | ___ame | ___eigh | ___est | ___ose |

***Now go to the Progress Chart to record your score!*** Total 80

# Paper 3

Look at these groups of words.

| A | B | C |
|---|---|---|
| Trees | Food | Birds |

Choose the correct group for each of the words below. Write in the letter.

**1–5** parrot ___ 　 pine ___ 　 broccoli ___ 　 willow ___ 　 eagle ___

beans ___ 　 noodles ___ 　 wren ___ 　 robin ___ 　 oak ___

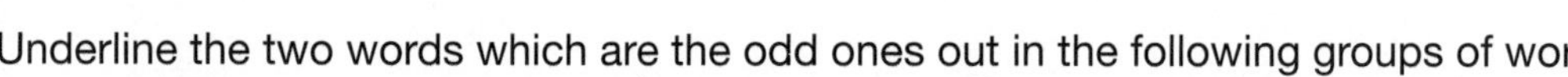

Underline the two words which are the odd ones out in the following groups of words.

| **Example** | black | <u>king</u> | purple | green | <u>house</u> |
|---|---|---|---|---|---|
| **6** | idea | thought | clever | notion | dull |
| **7** | divide | join | subtract | unite | combine |
| **8** | nearby | remote | neighbouring | foreign | distant |
| **9** | compel | lively | force | pressure | sad |
| **10** | hint | lie | complaint | sign | indication |

Find the letter which will end the first word and start the second word. B 10

**Example** peac ( h ) ome

11 mos ( ___ ) alt

12 jum ( ___ ) lum

13 gla ( ___ ) eck

14 sol ( ___ ) nion

15 win ( ___ ) nit 5

Complete the following sentences by selecting the most sensible word from each group of words given in the brackets. Underline the words selected. B 14

**Example** The (children, books, foxes) carried the (houses, books, steps) home from the (greengrocer, library, factory).

16 We all need (books, food, soap) to help build a (healthy, cold, solid) (garden, air, body).

17 A (lion, giraffe, crocodile) can eat the (leaves, rice, meat) from the (highest, fastest, tidiest) part of the tree.

18 Never (fly, sing, stand) under a (tree, bird, aeroplane) during a thunderstorm.

19 He left after (lunch, breakfast, midnight) on a (rainy, summery, hot) November (year, night, Christmas).

20 She (cried, asked, whispered) her (dog, toy, mother) before using her new (computer, walk, house). 5

Underline the pair of words most opposite in meaning. B 9

| | | | |
|---|---|---|---|
| **Example** | cup, mug | coffee, milk | hot, cold |
| 21 | danger, risk | notice, remark | guilty, innocent |
| 22 | exact, true | slow, swift | connect, link |
| 23 | joy, sorrow | uncover, open | mistake, error |
| 24 | floppy, hanging | hazard, safety | alike, same |
| 25 | accurate, wrong | roomy, spacious | lap, circuit |

5

Complete the following expressions by filling in the missing word. B 15

**Example** Pen is to ink as brush is to paint.

26 Mother is to father as ______________ is to son.

27 Century is to hundred as dozen is to ______________.

28 Find is to fine as mind is to ______________.

29 Flock is to sheep as ______________ is to cows.

30 January is to December as Tuesday is to ______________. 5

Find a word that can be put in front of each of the following words to make new, compound words. B 11

| | | | | | |
|---|---|---|---|---|---|
| | **Example** | cast | fall | ward | pour | down |
| **31** | boat | buoy | guard | jacket | _______ |
| **32** | gap | over | watch | page | _______ |
| **33** | guard | fighter | fly | power | _______ |
| **34** | work | land | pecker | worm | _______ |
| **35** | ache | stroke | ward | date | _______ |

5

Underline the one word in the brackets which will go equally well with both the pairs of words outside the brackets. B 5

| | | | |
|---|---|---|---|
| **Example** | rush, attack | cost, fee | (price, hasten, strike, <u>charge</u>, money) |
| **36** ice, chill | | stop, standstill | (cold, fix, freeze, wintry, halt) |
| **37** team, gang | | edge, margin | (party, side, limit, area, support) |
| **38** boring, uninteresting | | gloomy, cloudy | (clear, weather, exciting, dull, work) |
| **39** here, attending | | gift, donation | (guest, charity, ready, present, show) |
| **40** find, hunt | | path, trail | (train, track, sniff, catch, line) |

5

Thomas, Kasim, Charlotte and Elena all have sandwiches in their lunchboxes. B 25
Most of the children prefer healthy snacks.
Elena has a pear and Kasim has an apple.
Thomas, Charlotte and Elena have yogurts.
Elena was running late for school and is the only child who has forgotten to bring a drink.
Kasim has a snack bar in case he still feels hungry.

**41** How many children have sandwiches, yogurt and a drink for lunch? _______

**42** Which two children have the same items for lunch? _______________

**43** Which child has the most items in their lunchbox? _______________

3

Fill in the crosswords so that all the given words are included. You have been given one letter as a clue in each crossword. B 19

**44–45**

| | | | | | |
|---|---|---|---|---|---|
| | ■ | | ■ | | ■ |
| | | | | | |
| | ■ | | ■ | | ■ |
| | | | | | |
| | ■ | | ■ | | ■ |
| | I | | | | |

stamps, angers, disuse, nested, extend, timber

**46–47**

| | | | | | |
|---|---|---|---|---|---|
| ■ | | ■ | | ■ | |
| | | | | | |
| ■ | | ■ | L | ■ | |
| | | | | | |
| ■ | | ■ | | ■ | |
| | | | | | |

messed, prised, antler, pilots, inside, floods

4

If < £ > < / ? $ £ is the code for SENSIBLE what do these codes stand for? B 24

**48** < £ > < £ ________

**49** $ / > £ ________

**50** $ £ < < ________

What are the codes for the following words?

**51** BINS ________

**52** BLISS ________ 5

Give the two missing numbers in the following sequences. B 23

**Example** 2 4 6 8 10 12

**53** 17 21 __ 29 __ 37

**54** 15 __ 20 18 __ 27

**55** 96 48 24 12 __ __

**56** 47 __ 41 38 35 __

**57** 14 23 33 __ 56 __ 5

modem monster model mould mobile

If these words were placed in alphabetical order, which word would come: B 20

**58** second? ________

**59** last? ________

**60** first? ________ 3

Find the four-letter word hidden at the end of one word and the beginning of the next word. The order of the letters may not be changed. B 21

**Example** The children had bats and balls. sand

**61** Sometimes I wash old golf balls then resell them. ________

**62** Some of the buses went on but mine stopped at the corner. ________

**63** We are going to paint your room this weekend. ________

**64** The missing cat eventually came home. ________

**65** Everyone at my office begins at nine. ________ 5

Rearrange the muddled letters in capitals to make a proper word. The answer will complete the sentence sensibly. B 16

**Example** A BEZAR is an animal with stripes. ZEBRA

**66–67** They climbed the ERET at the TTMOOB of the garden. ________ ________

**68** Dark clouds usually bring IANR. ________

**69–70** Switch your THILG off by NENI. ________ ________ 5

Underline the one word which **cannot be made** from the letters of the word in capital letters. B 7

**Example** STATIONERY stone tyres ration <u>nation</u> noisy

| | | | | | | |
|---|---|---|---|---|---|---|
| 71 | DESCRIPTION | cried | snort | nicer | pride | preen |
| 72 | BREAKDOWN | brand | wander | dream | rowed | brown |
| 73 | PLASTERING | staring | string | laser | grass | strain |
| 74 | BANNISTER | banter | stern | nasty | rinse | tribe |
| 75 | SILHOUETTE | house | those | teeth | heels | honest |

5

Find the three-letter word which can be added to the letters in capitals to make a new word. The new word will complete the sentence sensibly. B 22

**Example** The cat sprang onto the MO. <u>USE</u>

76 On Saturday they went to the nursery to buy some PLS. ________

77 She only managed to write a couple of SENCES. ________

78 Take that out of your MH! ________

79 The mobile phone TERY was low. ________

80 SHAR your pencils please. ________

5

***Now go to the Progress Chart to record your score!*** Total 80

# Paper 4

Underline two words, one from each group, that go together to form a new word. The word in the first group always comes first. B 8

**Example** (hand, <u>green</u>, for) (light, <u>house</u>, sure)

1 (birthday, card, best) (week, fun, board)

2 (we, his, my) (sister, self, own)

3 (no, yes, nice) (thanks, there, thing)

4 (bread, butter, knife) (cup, fork, spread)

5 (rug, mat, go) (door, by, stick)

5

Add one letter to the word in capital letters to make a new word. The meaning of the new word is given in the clue. B 12

| | | | |
|---|---|---|---|
| **Example** | PLAN | simple | plain |
| **6** | PIECE | make a hole | ________ |
| **7** | FIN | not rainy | ________ |
| **8** | ONE | on one occasion | ________ |
| **9** | LOSE | unfastened | ________ |
| **10** | MAN | unkind | ________ |

5

Underline the one word in the brackets which will go equally well with both the pairs of words outside the brackets. B 5

| | | | |
|---|---|---|---|
| **Example** | rush, attack | cost, fee | (price, hasten, strike, charge, money) |
| **11** club, diamond | hoe, rake | | (weapon, spade, jewel, garden, heart) |
| **12** bracelet, necklace | telephone, bell | | (wedding, ring, line, valuable, rich) |
| **13** toss, throw | actors, players | | (grab, role, project, catch, cast) |
| **14** cosy, at ease | well-off, wealthy | | (easy, rich, comfortable, helpful, happy) |
| **15** decrease, reduce | ignore, unimportant | | (share, sale, allow, discount, bother) |

5

Underline the two words which are the odd ones out in the following groups of words. B 4

| | | | | | |
|---|---|---|---|---|---|
| **Example** | black | king | purple | green | house |
| **16** | run | trainer | walk | sock | jog |
| **17** | hot | roast | grill | spicy | toast |
| **18** | plan | idea | organize | drawing | prepare |
| **19** | cub | cat | gosling | lamb | goat |
| **20** | orange | brown | grass | lemon | cherry |

5

Alice catches the bus at 7:15 am and arrives at her destination 1 hour 30 minutes later. B 25

Her journey takes twice as long as Grace's.

Lucy's bus leaves at 7:45 am and her journey takes 20 minutes.

Grace's bus leaves at 7:30 am.

**21** At what time does Alice complete her journey? ________

**22** At what time does Grace's bus reach its destination? ________

**23** At what time does Lucy's journey end? ________ 3

Give the two missing numbers in the following sequences. B 23

| | | | | | | |
|---|---|---|---|---|---|---|
| **Example** | 2 | 4 | 6 | 8 | 10 | 12 |
| **24** | 17 | ___ | ___ | 23 | 25 | 27 |
| **25** | 11 | 14 | 22 | 16 | ___ | ___ |
| **26** | ___ | 4 | 6 | 9 | 13 | ___ |
| **27** | 19 | 22 | 24 | ___ | ___ | 32 |
| **28** | ___ | 5 | 3 | ___ | 4 | 15 |

5

Find the three-letter word which can be added to the letters in capitals to make a new word. The new word will complete the sentence sensibly. B 22

**Example** The cat sprang onto the MO. USE

**29** She FED her mug with tea. ________

**30** When it's hot, my dog lies in the SE. ________

**31** Children usually prefer SY beaches. ________

**32** SUDLY, I wanted to go. ________

**33** The book is on the SH. ________

5

Underline the pair of words most opposite in meaning. B 9

| | | | |
|---|---|---|---|
| **Example** | cup, mug | coffee, milk | hot, cold |
| **34** | forest, wood | true, false, | mild, gentle |
| **35** | student, pupil | car, auto | rear, front |
| **36** | visit, call | cheeky, polite | child, infant |
| **37** | allow, deny | marry, join | dig, burrow |
| **38** | change, swap | same, alike | total, partial |

5

Find the letter which will end the first word and start the second word. B 10

**Example** peac ( h ) ome

**39** luc ( ___ ) iss

**40** bul ( ___ ) ell

**41** gro ( ___ ) asp

**42** fol ( ___ ) erb

**43** oa ( ___ ) race

5

Read the first two statements and then underline one of the four options below that must be true. B 25

**44** 'Fish breathe underwater. Goldfish are a common type of pet fish.'

Goldfish make good pets.

The seas are full of fish.

Goldfish breathe underwater.

Fish live in salt water.

Read the first two statements and then underline one of the four options below that must be true.

**45** 'Bees make honey. Honey tastes sweet.'

Bees are sweet.

Everyone likes honey.

Bees make sweet honey.

Bees can sting.

Read the first two statements and then underline one of the four options below that must be true.

**46** 'Some shoes are made from leather. Leather is waterproof.'

Shoes are worn with socks.

All shoes are made from leather.

Leather shoes are waterproof.

Leather is the best material for shoes. 3

Fill in the crosswords so that all the given words are included. You have been given one letter as a clue in each crossword. B 19

**47–48**

better, cheeky, trying, yogurt, exists, hordes

**49–50**

litter, glides, recede, strain, drawer, sunset 4

Fill in the missing letters. The alphabet has been written out to help you. B 23

A B C D E F G H I J K L M N O P Q R S T U V W X Y Z

**Example** AB is to CD as PQ is to RS.

**51** CN is to DO as HR is to ______.

**52** HF is to JD as MW is to ______.

**53** CBE is to DAF as PNS is to ______.

**54** BD is to EG as RT is to ______.

**55** LCF is to KBE as TXQ is to ______. 5

knead knight knick kneeing kneecap B 20

If these words were put in alphabetical order, which one would come:

**56** third? __________

**57** fourth? __________

If the words were listed in reverse in alphabetical order, which one would come:

**58** first? __________

**59** last? __________

**60** fourth? __________ 5

If ? & $ * ! £ @ > < is the code for COMPUTERS, what do these codes stand for? B 24

**61** < £ & > @ __________

**62** $ & < £ __________

**63** ? & ! > < @ __________

What are the codes for the following words?

**64** TERM __________

**65** CUTE __________ 5

Underline the two words which are made from the same letters. B 7

| | | | | | | |
|---|---|---|---|---|---|---|
| | **Example** | TAP | PET | TEA | POT | EAT |
| **66** | NAME | AMEND | DREAM | MEAN | MADE | NEAR |
| **67** | TAPS | STARE | SNAP | TAPE | PANT | PANS |
| **68** | MILLS | MILES | SLIME | SAWN | WARM | WORM |
| **69** | MARCH | CHANT | WEAR | CHARM | WATCH | MARSH |
| **70** | SEVEN | PHRASE | SHAPE | GRAPH | PHASE | SEVER |

5

Find and underline the two words which need to change places for each sentence to make sense. B 17

**Example** She went to letter the write.

**71** Dad drives to us school in the car.

**72** She had knee her cut badly.

**73** I have to wait and sit.

**74** Mum knows we trick planning to were her.

**75** We cash to the bank to get some went. 5

If s = 3, e = 2, r = 5, a = 1, t = 6 and d = 4, find the value of the following words by adding the letters together.

B 26

**76** rested ______

**77** read ______

**78** treat ______

**79** stared ______

**80** deer ______

5

***Now go to the Progress Chart to record your score!*** **Total** 80

# Paper 5

Remove one letter from the word in capital letters to leave a new word. The meaning of the new word is given in the clue.

B 12

**Example** AUNT an insect <u>ant</u>

**1** DOZEN sleep ______

**2** TIRED joined ______

**3** SPOUT place ______

**4** BOUND connection ______

**5** PLEASANT bumpkin ______

5

Underline the two words, one from each group, which are closest in meaning.

B 3

**Example** (race, shop, <u>start</u>) (finish, <u>begin</u>, end)

**6** (hit, punch, hand) (success, fail, nervous)

**7** (behave, complication, rule) (quiz, mood, problem)

**8** (cheap, price, buy) (fee, purse, sell)

**9** (mind, real, imagine) (eye, suppose, copy)

**10** (test, proof, try) (lies, tell, evidence)

5

Find the missing number by using the two numbers outside the brackets in the same way as the other sets of numbers.

B 14

**Example** 2 [8] 4 3 [18] 6 5 [25] 5

**11** 9 [47] 5 3 [8] 2 12 [ ___ ] 3

**12** 12 [2] 6 81 [9] 9 24 [ ___ ] 12

13 13 [30] 12 12 [29] 12 7 [____] 12

14 9 [4] 4 7 [2] 4 10 [____] 4

15 16 [32] 2 8 [24] 3 7 [____] 3

5

Find the letter which will complete both pairs of words, ending the first word and starting the second. The same letter must be used for both pairs of words.

B 10

**Example** mea ( t ) able fi ( t ) ub

16 tria (____) ead rea (____) ight

17 pla (____) es tr (____) ellow

18 brin (____) host ran (____) rim

19 bul (____) lack cri (____) ald

20 foo (____) emper sal (____) hank

5

Underline the one word in the brackets which will go equally well with both the pairs of words outside the brackets.

B 5

**Example** rush, attack cost, fee (price, hasten, strike, <u>charge</u>, money)

21 practise, rehearse dig, pierce (roll, drill, wind, turn, study)

22 oar, pole dabble, splash (steer, wade, waves, paddle, river)

23 review, inspect stop, limit (examine, check, confirm, halt, accept)

24 explode, roar success, growth (thunder, echo, boom, crash, strong)

25 strength, energy make, cause (power, force, health, encourage, require)

5

Underline the one word which **cannot be made** from the letters of the word in capital letters.

B 7

**Example** STATIONERY stone tyres ration <u>nation</u> noisy

26 TELEPHONES shone pole photo honest spent

27 STATUES astute suet uses sauce states

28 PETRIFIES fires feast spite trees rites

29 CHRISTMAS smith chasm match charm start

30 RADISHES shade rashes dress shares drains

5

Find a word that is similar in meaning to the word in capital letters and that rhymes with the second word. B 5

**Example** CABLE tyre wire

31 APPLAUD strap ______

32 ORDINARY train ______

33 BANQUET least ______

34 EMPLOY choir ______

35 LONGING burn ______ 5

Find the four-letter word hidden at the end of one word and the beginning of the next word. The order of the letters may not be changed. B 21

**Example** The children had bats and balls. sand

36 The clock struck twelve and minutes later we left. ______

37 The best emeralds are used for jewellery. ______

38 Some of his ideas were a bit unusual. ______

39 Some people find it hard to admit when they are wrong. ______

40 We made sure that no one missed their turn. ______ 5

Change the first word into the last word by changing one letter at a time and making a new, different word in the middle. B 13

**Example** CASE CASH LASH

41 WILL ______ WIND

42 PITH ______ WISH

43 HALL ______ SALT

44 OXEN ______ EVEN

45 KIND ______ BAND 5

Complete the following expressions by underlining the missing word. B 15

**Example** Frog is to tadpole as swan is to (duckling, baby, cygnet).

46 Nimble is to agile as calm is to (excited, violent, still).

47 Soothe is to disturb as enjoy is to (adore, dislike, appreciate).

48 Grim is to pleasant as numerous is to (many, numbers, sparse).

49 Pleased is to delighted as greet is to (card, ignore, welcome).

50 Seldom is to often as descend is to (go, arrive, rise). 5

Fill in the crosswords so that all the given words are included. You have been given one letter as a clue in each crossword.

B 19

**51–52**

| | | | | | |
|---|---|---|---|---|---|
| | | | | | |
| | | | | | |
| | | | | | |
| | | | | | |
| | | M | | | |

simple, arrive, temple, cement
preens, aspect

**53–54**

| | | | | | |
|---|---|---|---|---|---|
| | | V | | | |
| | | | | | |
| | | | | | |
| | | | | | |
| | | | | | |

adders, reveal, revert, revere
styles, beheld

**55–56**

| | | | | | |
|---|---|---|---|---|---|
| | | | | | |
| | | | | | |
| | | | | O | |
| | | | | | |
| | | | | | |

nation, active, octave, finish
leaner, tether

6

Give the two missing numbers in the following sequences.

B 23

| | | | | | | | |
|---|---|---|---|---|---|---|---|
| | **Example** | 2 | 4 | 6 | 8 | 10 | 12 |
| **57** | 16 | 20 | 25 | ___ | 34 | 38 | ___ |
| **58** | ___ | 64 | 56 | ___ | 40 | 32 | 24 |
| **59** | 85 | ___ | 61 | 52 | ___ | 40 | 37 |
| **60** | 6 | ___ | 12 | 20 | 18 | 30 | ___ |

4

A B C D E F G H I J K L M N O P Q R S T U V W X Y Z

B 24

Solve the problems by working out the letter codes.

**61** If the code for BEAT is CFBU, what is the code for MICE? ________

**62** If the code for TEST is VGUV, what is the code for JUMP? ________

**63** If the code for SKATE is RJZSD, what is the code for LINE? ________

**64** If the code for CONSIDER is AMLQGBCP, what does the code NSPQC stand for? ________

**65** If the code for ALTER is BMUFS, what does the code ZPVOH stand for? ________

5

If A = 2, B = 4, C = 5, D = 10 and E = 8, give the answers to these calculations as letters. B 26

66 B + E − A = ___

67 D × A ÷ B = ___

68 (E + B) − D = ___

69 C × A = ___

70 (D − B) + (E ÷ B) = ___

71 (B × A) − (A × A) = ___ 6

Tom's hamster is 7 years younger than his cat. His dog, who is twice the age of the hamster, will be 7 next year. B 25

72 How old is Tom's cat? ______ 1

73 Write the letters of the word TADPOLE in the order in which they appear in the dictionary. B 20

___ ___ ___ ___ ___ ___ ___ 1

74 If the letters in the following word are arranged in alphabetical order, which letter comes in the middle? B 20

MOVED ___ 1

75 If the months of the year were arranged in alphabetical order, which month would come third? B 20

______ 1

Imagine each of these words spelled backwards, then write the number below each word to indicate if it would be 1st, 2nd, 3rd or 4th in alphabetical order. B 20

| | | | | |
|---|---|---|---|---|
| 76 | taught | thought | naughty | daughter |
| | ______ | ______ | ______ | ______ |
| 77 | suit | fruit | juice | nuisance |
| | ______ | ______ | ______ | ______ |
| 78 | fabulous | anxious | famous | enormous |
| | ______ | ______ | ______ | ______ |
| 79 | illness | happiness | fitness | clumsiness |
| | ______ | ______ | ______ | ______ |
| 80 | terrible | squirrel | horrible | wheel |
| | ______ | ______ | ______ | ______ |

5

*Now go to the Progress Chart to record your score!* Total 80

# Paper 6

Give the two missing pairs of letters in the following sequences. The alphabet has been written out to help you. B 23

A B C D E F G H I J K L M N O P Q R S T U V W X Y Z

| | | | | | | |
|---|---|---|---|---|---|---|
| **Example** | CQ | DP | EQ | FP | GQ | HP |
| **1** ML | ___ | IH | GF | ___ | CB | |
| **2** BC | DI | GN | ___ | PU | ___ | |
| **3** AZ | ___ | EV | ___ | IR | KP | |
| **4** KL | JM | ___ | HO | GP | ___ | |
| **5** ZY | AB | XW | CD | ___ | ___ | |

5

Fill in the crosswords so that all the given words are included. You have been given one letter as a clue in each crossword. B 19

**6–7**

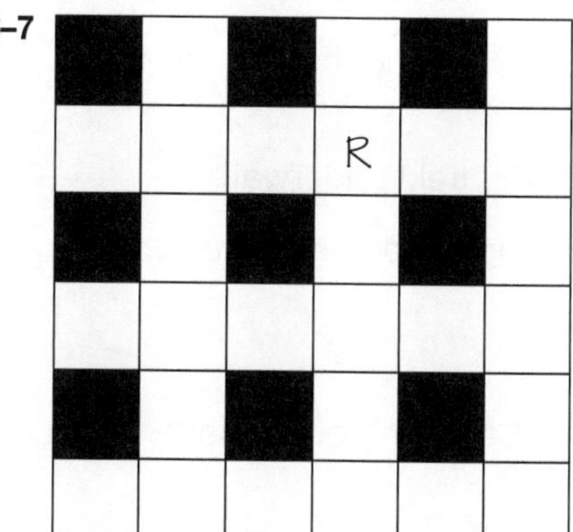

bearer, graded, eloped, triple, teller, friend

**8–9**

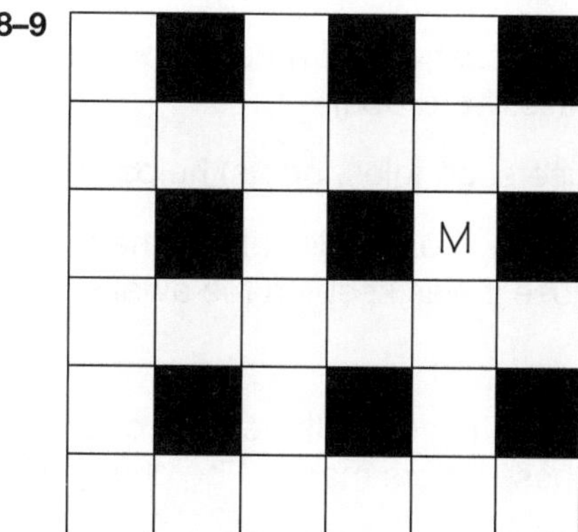

assume, banana, avenue, immune, ushers, answer

**10–11**

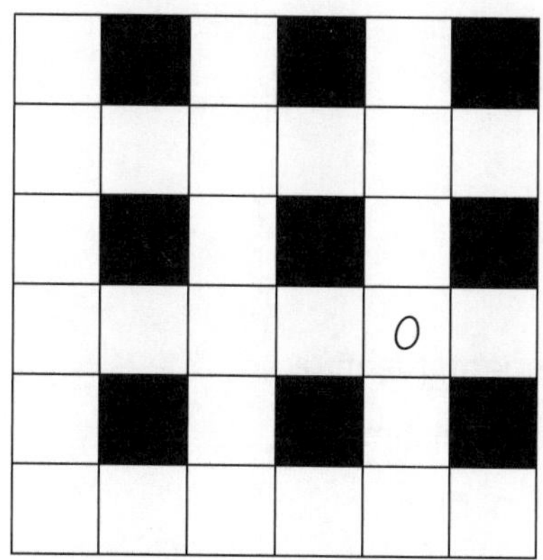

sunset, become, angles, needed, season, lesson

6

Find two letters which will end the first word and start the second word. B 10

**Example** rea ( c h ) air

12 nett ( ___ ___ ) opard

13 roa ( ___ ___ ) ing

14 form ( ___ ___ ) rand

15 glo ( ___ ___ ) ware

16 opti ( ___ ___ ) ion 5

Complete the following sentences by selecting the most sensible word from each group of words given in the brackets. Underline the words selected. B 14

**Example** The (children, books, foxes) carried the (houses, books, steps) home from the (greengrocer, library, factory).

17 It was my (turn, problem, behaviour) to (swim, ride, walk) the (car, bike, trampoline).

18 We (picked, said, made) some (bread, strawberries, jam) in the (sand, river, field).

19 Please (wet, dry, dust) the (furniture, flowers, plates) before putting them in the (cupboard, case, wardrobe).

20 Wearing (trousers, goggles, boots) helps you to (swim, ride, trek) underwater.

21 I had to (complain, wonder, lie) about the (pleasant, exciting, loud) (treat, music, money) because it was keeping me awake. 5

Find the four-letter word hidden at the end of one word and the beginning of the next word. The order of these letters may not be changed. B 21

**Example** The children had bats and balls. sand

22 Amy immediately posted her cards as she addressed them. ________

23 William, please come at once. ________

24 The sunset bathed the mountain in golden light. ________ 3

Underline the pair of words most similar in meaning. B 5

**Example** come, go roam, wander fear, fare

| | | |
|---|---|---|
| 25 rapid, slow | hide, seek | abundant, plentiful |
| 26 rare, common | answer, reply | prize, punishment |
| 27 transcend, translate | nothing, everything | rhythm, beat |
| 28 alter, change | lead, follow | protect, attack |
| 29 costly, cheap | injury, damage | famous, unknown |

5

Hannah and Charlie live in the country.
Charlie and Raj like going to the cinema.
Raj and Daisy live in a town and go to Drama Club.

B 25

**30** Who lives in a town and likes going to the cinema? ________ 1

If the code for PREVIOUS is 79643582, what do these codes stand for? B 24

**31** 2896 ________

**32** 78926 ________

**33** 9576 ________

**34** If the code for PRETEND is TUVWVYZ, what is the code for RENT? ________

**35** If the code for SHADE is 24536, what word is 4653? ________ 5

If S = 3, E = 2, R = 5, A = 1, T = 6 and D = 4, find the value of the following. B 26

**36** T + E + A = ________

**37** (R × E) + (S × T) = ________

**38** (S + T) − (A × R) = ________

**39** (S × E) ÷ (A × T) = ________

**40** Find the value of DRESSER by adding the letters together. ________ 5

Find the three-letter word which can be added to the letters in capitals to make a new word. The new word will complete the sentence sensibly. B 22

**Example** The cat sprang onto the MO. USE

**41** My PNTS encourage me to play outside. ________

**42–43** I packed lots of warm CLOS, but forgot my SPERS so my feet were cold.

________ ________

**44–45** The GES were fine but the bananas hadn't yet RIED. ________ ________ 5

Underline the word in the brackets closest in meaning to the word in capitals. B 5

**Example** UNHAPPY (unkind death laughter sad friendly)

**46** COLLECTION (hobby scrapbook assortment interesting valuable)

**47** COACH (trip driver school child instructor)

**48** EXTERIOR (paint fence inside outside private)

**49** STABLE (horses hay wobbly fixed shaky)

**50** MIX (divide cake blend fork icing) 5

Change the first word into the last word by changing one letter at a time and making two new, different words in the middle. B 13

| | | | | |
|---|---|---|---|---|
| **Example** | TEAK | TEAT | TENT | RENT |
| **51** CALM | ______ | ______ | POLE | |
| **52** LARK | ______ | ______ | HAZE | |
| **53** WAIT | ______ | ______ | JARS | |
| **54** SITE | ______ | ______ | BILL | |
| **55** DOZE | ______ | ______ | MADE | |

5

Change one word so that the sentence makes sense. Underline the word you are taking out and write your new word on the line. B 14

**Example** I waited in line to buy a book to see the film. ticket

**56** You should always wear a safety cap when riding a bicycle. ______

**57** She put her car in the garden every night. ______

**58** Copy the poem again; your trying isn't neat enough. ______

**59** The moon was shining by midday, so he ate his lunch in the garden. ______

**60** We sit in the garden until dark during the long days of winter. ______

5

Move one letter from the first word and add it to the second word to make two new words. B 13

| | | | |
|---|---|---|---|
| **Example** hunt | sip | hut | snip |
| **61** through | fog | ______ | ______ |
| **62** boat | muse | ______ | ______ |
| **63** tray | hem | ______ | ______ |
| **64** blend | back | ______ | ______ |
| **65** cheat | last | ______ | ______ |

5

Find a word that can be put in front of each of the following words to make new, compound words. B 11

| | | | | |
|---|---|---|---|---|
| **Example** cast | fall | ward | pour | down |
| **66** skirts | side | line | burst | ______ |
| **67** on | date | roar | set | ______ |
| **68** go | take | line | growth | ______ |
| **69** spoon | cake | time | cup | ______ |
| **70** box | card | code | age | ______ |

5

Which word in each group contains only the first six letters of the alphabet? B 18

| | | | | | |
|---|---|---|---|---|---|
| **Example** | defeat | farce | abide | deaf | dice |
| **71** | badge | deck | bead | beach | fake |
| **72** | cage | deal | cake | fade | beak |
| **73** | ease | debacle | decade | fable | each |
| **74** | cuff | bean | calf | bake | café |
| **75** | edge | fail | face | feel | edge |

5

Look at these groups of words. B 1

| A | B | C |
|---|---|---|
| Clothing | Coast | Calendar |

Choose the correct group for each of the words below. Write in the letter.

**76–79** sand ____ diving ____ linen ____ cliffs ____

era ____ waistcoat ____ annual ____ monday ____ 4

Read the first two statements and then underline one of the four options below that must be true. B 25

**80** 'A monkey is an animal. Some monkeys live in the rainforests.'

Most monkeys live in rainforests.
A rainforest is a hot place.
Some animals live in rainforests.
Monkeys climb trees. 1

***Now go to the Progress Chart to record your score!*** **Total** 80

# Paper 7

PROVOKE PROVINCE PROSPER PROVISION PROSPECT B 20

If these words were placed in alphabetical order, which one would come:

**1** first? ________

**2** last? ________

**3** middle? ________

**4** fourth? ________

**5** second? ________ 5

Underline one word in the brackets which is most opposite in meaning to the word in capitals. B 6

**Example** WIDE (broad vague long <u>narrow</u> motorway)

6 STALE (bread crisp tasteless flat boring)

7 SPEAKER (teacher lawyer politician listener leader)

8 BUSY (active routine idle occupied service)

9 EXTEND (build reach shorten amount line)

10 BREAK (divide limb news connect fracture) 5

Find the three-letter word which can be added to the letters in capitals to make a new word. The new word will complete the sentence sensibly. B 22

**Example** The cat sprang onto the MO. <u>USE</u>

11 She was DISTRED by the constant noise and found it hard to study. ________

12 That's a BRIANT idea! ________

13 I've THN my old shoes away. ________

14 Why aren't you ALLD to come over? ________

15 Let's grab a bite to eat BEE the film. ________ 5

Which one letter can be added to the front of all of these words to make new words? B 12

**Example** <u>c</u>are <u>c</u>at <u>c</u>rate <u>c</u>all

16 __ife __ight __ice __oad __urk

17 __ast __ine __ume __ield __ilm

18 __ave __ear __ush __ort __aste

19 __all __and __unch __ook __elm

20 __able __ast __oast __old __ube 5

Move one letter from the first word and add it to the second word to make two new words. B 13

**Example** hunt sip <u>hut</u> <u>snip</u>

21 fair deal ________ ________

22 chilly earn ________ ________

23 stage suck ________ ________

24 cover dawn ________ ________

25 feud pond ________ ________ 5

## Paper 1

1 queue, visitors
2 Not, she
3 bones, dogs
4 get, to
5 Out, he
6 vanish
7 noisy
8 descend
9 fancy
10 solid
11–15 trout D; satsuma B; kiwi B; weasel A; rounders C; salmon D; cheetah A; lacrosse C; plaice D; badminton C
16 anteater
17 laptop
18 needless
19 friendship
20 broadcast
21 guess, suspect
22 option, choice
23 diminish, lessen
24 ruler, controller
25 job, task
26 tennis
27 B
28 C
29 A
30–33 *Give two marks for each correct crossword.*

| A | N | G | E | L |
|---|---|---|---|---|
| L | | R | | A |
| E | N | A | C | T |
| R | | C | | C |
| T | E | E | T | H |

| C | A | N | O | E |
|---|---|---|---|---|
| R | | I | | A |
| E | I | G | H | T |
| S | | H | | E |
| S | A | T | I | N |

34 KL
35 ON
36 GK
37 CE
38 XU
39 % ^ ~ £
40 ! ^ ~ %
41 % £ £ #
42 ! * £ ~ £
43 ~ ^ ^ %
44 James
45 Laura
46 Omar
47 Kate
48 Eva
49 Jacob
50 14, 18
51 24, 48
52 6, 9
53 9, 27
54 2, 15
55 t
56 m
57 t
58 e
59 d
60 STEP
61 LIVE
62 DEER
63 BAIL
64 GRAB
65 about
66 open
67 snap
68 faint
69 cross
70 Chairs can be made of wood.
71 wand
72 hear
73 chop
74 done
75 test
76 notice
77 nineteen
78 dated
79 hurry
80 drawer

## Paper 2

1 56, 28
2 16, 128
3 17, 13
4 17, 24
5 20, 16
6 17
7 3255
8 5274
9 7256
10 4256
11 5624
12 foal, calf
13 driver, pilot
14 hasten, gather
15 game, boss
16 jump, walk
17 CROSS
18 HOLIDAY
19 RULER
20 WRIST
21 PARTY
22 tip
23 skip
24 show
25 place
26 file
27 16
28 4
29 40
30 15
31 25
32 girl, mother, sweets
33 check, work, teacher
34 riding, horses, field
35 butter, sugar, eggs
36 sunny, hot, beach
37 crossroads
38 capsize
39 useless
40 seaweed
41 nearby
42 limb, crack
43 fort, party
44 play, crumbs
45 run, ideal
46 trust, shore
47 calm, still
48 beam, shine
49 scratch, graze
50 fair, honest
51 force, power
52 d
53 s
54 d
55 w
56 g
57 HIP
58 ICE
59 HOP
60 EAR
61 TOP
62–65 *Give two marks for each correct crossword.*

| A | L | O | F | T |
|---|---|---|---|---|
| G | | U | | R |
| R | I | N | S | E |
| E | | C | | A |
| E | X | E | R | T |

| S | O | C | K | S |
|---|---|---|---|---|
| T | | H | | A |
| A | C | O | R | N |
| M | | I | | D |
| P | A | R | T | Y |

66 YB, VE
67 KI, MK
68 ZEN, AFO
69 GP, ML
70 TE, FU
71 S
72 S
73 T
74 P
75 Q

76 b
77 j
78 f
79 w
80 n

## Paper 3

**1–5** parrot C; beans B; pine A; noodles B; broccoli B; wren C; willow A; robin C; eagle C; oak A
**6** clever, dull
**7** divide, subtract
**8** nearby, neighbouring
**9** lively, sad
**10** lie, complaint
**11** s
**12** p
**13** d
**14** o
**15** k
**16** food, healthy, body
**17** giraffe, leaves, highest
**18** stand, tree
**19** midnight, rainy, night
**20** asked, mother, computer
**21** guilty, innocent
**22** slow, swift
**23** joy, sorrow
**24** hazard, safety
**25** accurate, wrong
**26** daughter
**27** twelve
**28** mine
**29** herd
**30** Monday
**31** life
**32** stop
**33** fire
**34** wood
**35** back
**36** freeze
**37** side
**38** dull
**39** present
**40** track
**41** 2
**42** Thomas and Charlotte
**43** Kasim
**44–47** *Give two marks for each correct crossword.*

| N | | S | | A | |
|---|---|---|---|---|---|
| E | X | T | E | N | D |
| S | | A | | G | |
| T | I | M | B | E | R |
| E | | P | | R | |
| D | I | S | U | S | E |

| | A | | P | | M |
|---|---|---|---|---|---|
| I | N | S | I | D | E |
| | T | | L | | S |
| F | L | O | O | D | S |
| | E | | T | | E |
| P | R | I | S | E | D |

**48** SENSE
**49** LINE
**50** LESS
**51** ? / > <
**52** ? $ / < <
**53** 25, 33
**54** 9, 25
**55** 6, 3
**56** 44, 32
**57** 44, 69
**58** model
**59** mould
**60** mobile
**61** hold
**62** nest
**63** wear
**64** them
**65** neat
**66–67** TREE, BOTTOM
**68** RAIN
**69–70** LIGHT, NINE
**71** preen
**72** dream
**73** grass
**74** nasty
**75** honest
**76** ANT
**77** TEN
**78** OUT
**79** BAT
**80** PEN

## Paper 4

**1** cardboard
**2** myself
**3** nothing
**4** buttercup
**5** rugby
**6** PIERCE
**7** FINE
**8** ONCE
**9** LOOSE
**10** MEAN
**11** spade
**12** ring
**13** cast
**14** comfortable
**15** discount
**16** trainer, sock
**17** hot, spicy
**18** idea, drawing
**19** cat, goat
**20** brown, grass
**21** 8:45 am
**22** 8:15 am
**23** 8:05 am
**24** 19, 21
**25** 33, 18
**26** 3, 18
**27** 27, 29
**28** 2, 10
**29** ILL
**30** HAD
**31** AND
**32** DEN
**33** ELF
**34** true, false
**35** rear, front
**36** cheeky, polite
**37** allow, deny
**38** total, partial
**39** k
**40** b
**41** w
**42** k
**43** t
**44** Goldfish breathe underwater.
**45** Bees make sweet honey.
**46** Leather shoes are waterproof.
**47–50** *Give two marks for each correct crossword.*

| C | | T | | B | |
|---|---|---|---|---|---|
| H | O | R | D | E | S |
| E | | Y | | T | |
| E | X | I | S | T | S |
| K | | N | | E | |
| Y | O | G | U | R | T |

| G | | S | | R | |
|---|---|---|---|---|---|
| L | I | T | T | E | R |
| I | | R | | C | |
| D | R | A | W | E | R |
| E | | I | | D | |
| S | U | N | S | E | T |

**51** IS
**52** OU
**53** QMT
**54** UW
**55** SWP
**56** kneeing
**57** knick
**58** knight
**59** knead
**60** kneecap
**61** STORE

62 MOST
63 COURSE
64 £ @ > $
65 ? ! £ @
66 NAME, MEAN
67 SNAP, PANS
68 MILES, SLIME
69 MARCH, CHARM
70 SHAPE, PHASE
71 to, us
72 knee, cut
73 wait, sit
74 trick, were
75 cash, went
76 22
77 12
78 20
79 21
80 13

## Paper 5

1 doze
2 tied
3 spot
4 bond
5 peasant
6 hit, success
7 complication, problem
8 price, fee
9 imagine, suppose
10 proof, evidence
11 38
12 2
13 24
14 5
15 21
16 l
17 y
18 g
19 b
20 t
21 drill
22 paddle
23 check
24 boom
25 force
26 photo
27 sauce
28 feast
29 start
30 drains
31 clap
32 plain
33 feast
34 hire
35 yearn
36 slat
37 stem
38 side
39 toad
40 noon
41 WILD
42 WITH
43 HALT
44 OVEN
45 BIND
46 still
47 dislike
48 sparse
49 welcome
50 rise
51–56 *Give two marks for each correct crossword.*

|   | A |   | T |   | A |
|---|---|---|---|---|---|
| P | R | E | E | N | S |
|   | R |   | M |   | P |
| S | I | M | P | L | E |
|   | V |   | L |   | C |
| C | E | M | E | N | T |

|   | B |   | R |   | S |
|---|---|---|---|---|---|
| R | E | V | E | R | T |
|   | H |   | V |   | Y |
| R | E | V | E | A | L |
|   | L |   | R |   | E |
| A | D | D | E | R | S |

|   | O |   | F |   | L |
|---|---|---|---|---|---|
| A | C | T | I | V | E |
|   | T |   | N |   | A |
| N | A | T | I | O | N |
|   | V |   | S |   | E |
| T | E | T | H | E | R |

57 29, 43
58 72, 48
59 72, 45
60 10, 24
61 NJDF
62 LWOR
63 KHMD
64 PURSE
65 YOUNG
66 D
67 C
68 A
69 D
70 E
71 B
72 10
73 A D E L O P T
74 M
75 December
76 2 3 4 1
77 4 3 1 2
78 2 1 3 4
79 3 1 4 2
80 1 4 2 3

## Paper 6

1 KJ, ED
2 KR, VW
3 CX, GT
4 IN, FQ
5 VU, EF
6–11 *Give two marks for each correct crossword.*

|   | T |   | T |   | G |
|---|---|---|---|---|---|
| B | E | A | R | E | R |
|   | L |   | I |   | A |
| E | L | O | P | E | D |
|   | E |   | L |   | E |
| F | R | I | E | N | D |

| B |   | U |   | I |   |
|---|---|---|---|---|---|
| A | S | S | U | M | E |
| N |   | H |   | M |   |
| A | V | E | N | U | E |
| N |   | R |   | N |   |
| A | N | S | W | E | R |

| A |   | S |   | B |   |
|---|---|---|---|---|---|
| N | E | E | D | E | D |
| G |   | A |   | C |   |
| L | E | S | S | O | N |
| E |   | O |   | M |   |
| S | U | N | S | E | T |

12 le
13 st
14 er
15 be
16 on
17 turn, ride, bike
18 picked, strawberries, field
19 dry, plates, cupboard
20 goggles, swim
21 complain, loud, music
22 head
23 meat
24 them
25 abundant, plentiful
26 answer, reply
27 rhythm, beat
28 alter, change
29 injury, damage
30 Raj
31 SURE

32 PURSE
33 ROPE
34 UVYW
35 HEAD
36 9
37 28
38 4
39 1
40 24
41 ARE
42 THE
43 LIP
44 RAP
45 PEN
46 assortment
47 instructor
48 outside
49 fixed
50 blend
51 PALM PALE
52 HARK HARE
53 WART WARS
54 BITE BILE
55 DAZE MAZE
56 cap, helmet
57 garden, garage
58 trying, writing
59 moon, sun
60 winter, summer
61 though, frog
62 bat, mouse
63 ray, them
64 bend, black
65 chat, least
66 out
67 up
68 under
69 tea
70 post
71 bead
72 fade
73 decade
74 café
75 face
76–79 sand B; era C;
diving B; waistcoat A;
linen A; annual C;
cliffs B; Monday C
80 Some animals live in rainforests.

## Paper 7

1 PROSPECT
2 PROVOKE
3 PROVINCE
4 PROVISION
5 PROSPER
6 crisp
7 listener
8 idle
9 shorten
10 connect
11 ACT
12 ILL
13 ROW
14 OWE
15 FOR
16 l
17 f
18 p
19 h
20 c
21 far, ideal
22 chill, yearn
23 sage, stuck
24 cove, drawn
25 fed, pound
26 gpsl
27 tqppo
28 dvq
29 KNIFE
30 SAUCER
31 B
32 6752
33 2465
34 8236
35 64782
36 82465
37 courage, bravery
38 glance, look
39 halt, stop
40 cross, angry
41 tint, colour
42 brief, amazing
43 fruit, vegetable
44 listening, tasting
45 active, pity
46 fragile, squander
47 he
48 on
49 ce
50 us
51 in
52 ROBIN
53 CINEMA
54 MAGICIAN
55 CAMEL
56 COMMENCE
57 65, 36
58 24, 30
59 85, 103
60 125, 50
61 12, 16
62 SPIN
63 PIER
64 STAGE
65 CHEAT
66 TRAP
67 day, month
68 chair table
69 cheap, expensive
70 tail, claws
71 tea, water
72 was, in
73 form, each
74 from, some
75 on, up
76 made, admit
77–80 *Give two marks for each correct crossword.*

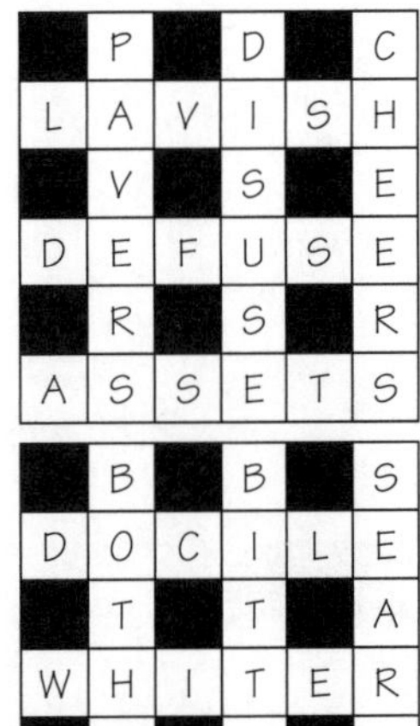


## Paper 8

1 tadpole
2 kind
3 keys
4 suggest
5 export
6 Water
7 Land
8 Day
9 Rain
10 Wind
11 snowdrop
12 wail
13 soar
14 spring
15 rain
16 RAT
17 WIN
18 OUR
19 TEN
20 EAT
21–24 *Give two marks for each correct crossword.*

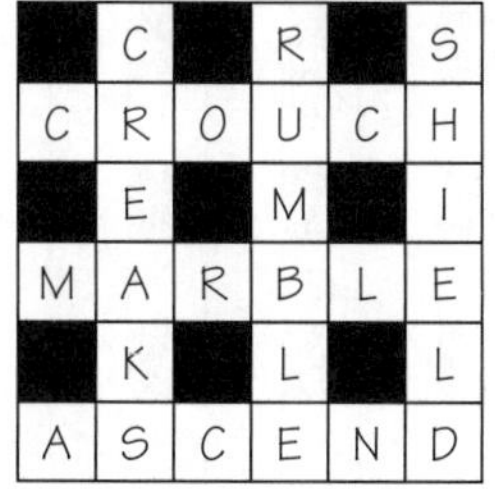


25 86253
26 25979
27 37527
28 93641
29 RAIL
30 REVEAL
31 TS, KJ
32 FR, GS
33 MH, KI
34 PT, UY
35 KO, QW
36 bleed
37 tests
38 overstay
39 ginger
40 leader
41 burnt, oven
42 Tired, sleep, school
43 dog, kennel, raining
44 question, plan, answer
45 pleased, holiday, summer
46 k
47 n
48 e
49 b
50 t
51 HAVE
52 NOSE
53 PALM
54 MOAN
55 STAR
56 DESIRE
57 DESCEND
58 DESCRIBE
59 D
60 9
61 7
62 2
63 10
64 9
65 Rings can be made of metal.
66 vague, certain
67 scatter, collect
68 satisfy, disappoint
69 undermine, enhance
70 unusual, ordinary
71 insect
72 throughout
73 nomad
74 attempt
75 beam
76 AMPYJ
77 CNKDK
78 RIGHT
79 ICUFTAY
80 BQDG

## Paper 9

1 MENTAL, LAMENT
2 STATE, TASTE
3 REWARD, DRAWER
4 CRATE, REACT
5 STOAT, TOAST
6 amount
7 stroll
8 difficult
9 scrape
10 talent
11 TOMB
12 GROUND
13 GARDEN
14 CYPRF
15 JMUCQR
16 twin
17 form
18 peel
19 heal
20 sour
21 open, closed
22 war, peace
23 alert, distracted
24 deliberate, accidental
25 essential, unimportant
26 flee, remain
27 mad, sane
28 Some animals in Africa feed on leaves.
29 Sounds can be represented by letters.
30–35 *Give two marks for each correct crossword.*

| L | A | P |
|---|---|---|
| E | G | O |
| D | O | T |

| T | O | E |
|---|---|---|
| W | A | Y |
| O | R | E |

| D | I | P |
|---|---|---|
| A | C | E |
| M | E | T |

36 6, 15
37 27, 37
38 55, 15
39 14, 22
40 28, 24
41 in
42 se
43 al
44 er
45 st
46 litre, kilogram
47 look, march
48 clear, weather
49 London, France
50 hinder, depress
51 rock
52 snappy
53 understanding
54 class
55 blossom
56 site
57 over
58 fate
59 sire
60 has
61 FADE
62 REAL
63 BRIEF
64 RAGE
65 LAPSE
66 go, cinema, week
67 autumn, leaves, fall
68 friends, play, park
69 parents, watching, television
70 clock, time, second
71 4356
72 5635
73 7254
74 6243
75 4273
76 get, stay
77 spent, saved
78 hair, teeth
79 songs, movies or films
80 hungry, thirsty

## Paper 10

1 NH, OI
2 KZ, PU
3 ID, FF
4 FV, CY
5 MP, NO
6 husband, wife
7 unite, join
8 pig, sty
9 spirited, vigorous
10 deny, admit
11 RAN
12 ONE
13 EAR
14 PEA
15 ASK
16 21
17 4
18 17
19 0
20 5
21 s
22 l
23 h

**24** d
**25** t
**26** guest
**27** limited
**28** drop
**29** approve
**30** genuine
**31** STAMP
**32** PROUD
**33** INVITED
**34** ACCIDENT
**35** PURSE
**36–39** *Give two marks for each correct crossword.*

| | C | | S | | A |
|---|---|---|---|---|---|
| L | O | I | T | E | R |
| | U | | A | | C |
| C | R | U | T | C | H |
| | S | | E | | E |
| C | E | N | S | O | R |

**40** Some people drink Chinese tea.
**41** 5361
**42** 1537
**43** 2845
**44** 6924
**45** 7824
**46** SEAT
**47** April
**48** crawl
**49** grain
**50** darts
**51** TRAP
**52** RISK
**53** PAST
**54** WAVE
**55** RIVAL
**56** share
**57** thrust
**58** voice
**59** clean
**60** swift
**61** TW
**62** CH
**63** NS
**64** QR
**65** RE
**66** justify, explain
**67** common, ordinary
**68** flood, overflow
**69** stale, old
**70** wreck, destroy
**71** able, life
**72** pot, frail
**73** stale, brush
**74** raft, cup
**75** grin, neat
**76** arrest, arrogant, artful, artificial, artistic
**77** exhibit, exhilarate, exile, expand, expectancy
**78** reason, reassure, rebel, rebuild, recite
**79** illegible, illicit, illogical, illusion, illustrate
**80** force, forcible, forecast, foreign, forever

## Paper 11

**1** FILE, FILL
**2** FIST, MIST
**3** SEAR, SEAL
**4** HERB, HERD
**5** LICE, VICE
**6** RACE, FACE
**7** pet, eat, overweight
**8** travel, rocket, astronauts
**9** teacher, report, improve
**10** cards, cats, dog
**11** note
**12** over
**13** flash
**14** bath
**15** under
**16** cheat
**17** tale
**18** sore
**19** dart
**20** paired
**21** wail
**22** than
**23** best
**24** mate
**25** stop
**26** leg
**27** serious
**28** outrageous
**29** edge
**30** reluctantly
**31–34** *Give two marks for each correct crossword.*

| | S | | R | | R |
|---|---|---|---|---|---|
| U | P | S | I | D | E |
| | R | | D | | P |
| M | E | D | D | L | E |
| | A | | L | | A |
| A | D | V | E | R | T |

**35** 5432
**36** 4216
**37** 3162
**38** 6145
**39** 1435
**40** 3265
**41** SE, WI
**42** I I, ME
**43** DS, ER
**44** 31, 40
**45** 56, 61
**46** negotiate, discuss
**47** support, assist
**48** peace, calm
**49** determined, persistent
**50** Tomorrow is Saturday.
**51** sh
**52** ma
**53** gh
**54** te
**55** se
**56** flight
**57** trim
**58** notice
**59** draw
**60** air
**61** nurse, medicine
**62** boredom, indifference
**63** glass, cup
**64** hunger, starving
**65** robin, ostrich
**66** ARCH
**67** LOCK
**68** REST
**69** TURN
**70** PORT
**71** panting
**72** pasty
**73** port
**74** sight
**75** quit
**76** DEPART, PARTED
**77** REMIT, MERIT
**78** SEVER, VERSE
**79** RETRACE, CATERER
**80** HORSE, SHORE

## Paper 12

**1** h
**2** d
**3** t

4 b
5 n
6 r
7 3 4 2 1
8 1 3 4 2
9 3 1 2 4
10 C
11 6
12 16
13 11
14–17 *Give two marks for each correct crossword.*

| D | E | W |
|---|---|---|
| O | W | E |
| G | E | T |

| S | U | M |
|---|---|---|
| E | R | A |
| E | N | D |

18 XLG
19 MVZG
20 URHS
21 appear, vanish
22 variety, routine
23 ready, unprepared
24 treasured, ignored
25 Not all dogs have name tags.
26 SERVE
27 UNITE
28 NEEDS
29 THREAD
30 LAMP
31 beginning, ending
32 croaks, roars
33 maximum, heavy
34 children, women
35 trustworthy, threaten
36 EARN
37 BOIL
38 DOWN
39 TIER
40 LOFT
41 BAND
42 FORM
43 LIST
44 WARD
45 MINT
46 aeroplane, car
47 lake, harbour
48 begin, start
49 compassionate, charitable
50 rubbish, insects
51 dairy, diary
52 hits, goals
53 adults, children
54 sum, word
55 toy, pet
56 exist
57 stroke
58 value
59 weary
60 mince
61 gentle, calm
62 cold, unfriendly
63 graceful, ballerina
64 prevent, allow
65 6472
66 8342
67 2415
68 BODY
69 BREAD
70 IMB
71 YTM
72 WV
73 NUJ
74 YV
75 GI, PR
76 BX, JP
77 UF, TG
78 33, 48
79 18, 13
80 26, 32

## Paper 13

1 tricky, faithful
2 reward, punishment
3 reject, accept
4 wing, paw
5 invented, actual
6 ban
7 have
8 slash
9 cave
10 path
11 reaction, response
12 spread, expand
13 fix, repair
14 degree, amount
15 hole, opening
16 15, 13
17 29, 64
18 8, 8
19 49, 64
20 20, 25
21 Claire and Amy
22 VDYH
23 OGURCIG
24 WINDY
25 Crows lay eggs.
26 st
27 te
28 me
29 pe
30 er
31 11
32 8
33 7
34 9
35 9
36 patch
37 weak
38 in
39 ate
40 bark
41 last
42 needle
43 land
44 state
45 tough
46 risk, bowl
47 band, harm
48 fame, camel
49 boar, draw
50 ton, mean
51 PL, SI
52 CX, FU
53 UE, SG
54 MN, UV
55 6341
56 6542
57 2463
58 5736
59 order
60 drove
61 POST
62 FERN
63 EVER
64 PINE
65 SAVE
66 MEAN
67 TEAM
68 DARE
69 STAR
70 THROB
71–74 *Give two marks for each correct crossword.*

| B | A | R |
|---|---|---|
| E | G | O |
| G | O | T |

| T | I | N |
|---|---|---|
| A | C | E |
| P | E | T |

75 wolf, howl
76 grab, snatch
77 crowded, deserted
78 glass, glasses
79 damage, harm
80 wave, sea

A B C D E F G H I J K L M N O P Q R S T U V W X Y Z

If the code for P L A T E is q m b u f, what are the codes for these words?

**26** FORK ______________

**27** SPOON ______________

**28** CUP ______________

What do these codes stand for?

**29** l o j g f ______________

**30** t b v d f s ______________

B 24 | 5

A, B, C, D and E are boats in a race. A is due south of C and due north west of B. D is west of A.

**31** Which boat is furthest east? ______________

B 25 | 1

Here are the number codes for four words. Match the right code to the right word.

| PUSH | HOPS | CHAP | POUCH |
|---|---|---|---|
| 2465 | 8236 | 6752 | 64782 |

**32** PUSH ______________

**33** HOPS ______________

**34** CHAP ______________

**35** POUCH ______________

**36** Write CHOPS in code. ______________

B 24 | 5

Underline the two words in each line which are most similar in type or meaning.

| | | | | | |
|---|---|---|---|---|---|
| **Example** | <u>dear</u> | pleasant | poor | extravagant | <u>expensive</u> |
| **37** coward | guilty | courage | bravery | tough | remedy |
| **38** face | glance | prevent | permit | look | suggest |
| **39** traffic | lights | halt | car | road | stop |
| **40** cross | stingy | generous | angry | loving | wealthy |
| **41** red | paper | paint | tint | artist | colour |

B 5 | 5

Complete the following sentences in the best way by choosing one word from each set of brackets.

**Example** Tall is to (tree, <u>short</u>, colour) as narrow is to (thin, white, <u>wide</u>).

**42** Short is to (shirt, maximum, brief) as incredible is to (believable, edible, amazing).

**43** Pear is to (fruit, tree, pair) as cabbage is to (soup, vegetable, sprout).

**44** Ear is to (ring, listening, noticed) as mouth is to (head, lips, tasting).

**45** Vigorous is to (active, athlete, feeble) as sympathy is to (crying, upset, pity).

**46** Tough is to (fragile, strict, harmless) as save is to (money, earn, squander).

B 15 | 5

Find two letters which will end the first word and start the second word. B 10

**Example** rea ( c h ) air

47 soot ( ___ ___ ) althy

48 up ( ___ ___ ) ce

49 offi ( ___ ___ ) real

50 circ ( ___ ___ ) ual

51 pla ( ___ ___ ) vent 5

Rearrange the muddled letters in capitals to make a proper word. The answer will complete the sentence sensibly. B 16

**Example** A BEZAR is an animal with stripes. ZEBRA

52 A NORIB is a type of bird. ________

53 Films are shown in a AMNICE. ________

54 A GIMANIAC does tricks with cards. ________

55 A LAECM doesn't need much water. ________

56 CEMNOCME means to begin. ________ 5

Give the two missing numbers in the following sequences. B 23

**Example** 2 4 6 8 10 12

57 75 28 70 32 ___ ___ 60

58 6 12 18 ___ ___ 36 42

59 73 75 79 ___ 93 ___ 115

60 175 150 ___ 100 75 ___ 25

61 6 8 9 12 ___ ___ 15 5

Rearrange the letters in capitals to make another word. The new word has something to do with the first two words. B 16

**Example** spot soil SAINT STAIN

62 turn swirl PINS ________

63 quay jetty RIPE ________

64 platform phase GATES ________

65 deceive trick TEACH ________

66 snare catch PART ________ 5

Change one word so that the sentence makes sense. Underline the word you are taking out and write your new word on the line. B 14

**Example** I waited in line to buy a book to see the film. ticket

67 The shortest day of the year is February. ____________

68 I reserved a chair for two at the restaurant. ____________

69 Her father complained that the telephone bill was too cheap. ____________

70 The kitten scratched her tail on our new chair. ____________

71 She boiled just enough tea in the kettle to make a hot drink. ____________ 5

Find and underline the two words which need to change places for each sentence to make sense. B 17

**Example** She went to letter the write.

72 Was which year in the big storm?

73 It is important that form each is filled in completely.

74 From friends some Australia are visiting.

75 We picked on shells up the beach.

76 I made that I have admit a mistake. 5

Fill in the crosswords so that all the given words are included. You have been given one letter as a clue in each crossword. B 19

77–78

| ■ |  | ■ |  | ■ |  |
|---|---|---|---|---|---|
|  |  |  |  |  |  |
| ■ |  | ■ | S | ■ |  |
|  |  |  |  |  |  |
| ■ |  | ■ |  | ■ |  |
|  |  |  |  |  |  |

defuse, pavers, assets, cheers, disuse, lavish

79–80

| ■ |  | ■ |  | ■ |  |
|---|---|---|---|---|---|
|  |  |  |  |  |  |
| ■ |  | ■ |  | ■ |  |
| W |  |  |  |  |  |
| ■ |  | ■ |  | ■ |  |
|  |  |  |  |  |  |

whiter, drench, bitten, search, bother, docile 4

*Now go to the Progress Chart to record your score!* Total 80

# Paper 8

Complete the following expressions by underlining the missing word. B 15

**Example** Frog is to tadpole as swan is to (duckling, baby, cygnet).

1 Butterfly is to caterpillar as frog is to (pond, tadpole, croak).

2 Vacant is to occupied as mean is to (selfish, person, kind).

3 Clock is to hands as piano is to (music, keys, instrument).

4 Fair is to just as imply is to (order, suggest, request).

5 Fact is to fiction as import is to (purchase, sell, export).

Find a word that can be put in front of each of the following words to make new, compound words.

| | | | | | |
|---|---|---|---|---|---|
| **Example** | cast | fall | ward | pour | down |
| 6 | cress | colour | fall | melon | ______ |
| 7 | lady | mark | slide | lord | ______ |
| 8 | light | break | dream | time | ______ |
| 9 | coat | bow | drop | fall | ______ |
| 10 | fall | burn | mill | break | ______ |

Underline the word in the brackets which goes best with the words outside the brackets.

**Example** word, paragraph, sentence (pen, cap, letter, top, stop)

11 daffodil, poppy, tulip (stem, plant, snowdrop, grow, garden)

12 shriek, howl, roar (sound, whisper, wail, conversation, noise)

13 climb, rise, ascend (shrink, arrive, movement, soar, descend)

14 autumn, winter, summer (year, Easter, calendar, spring, season)

15 hail, sleet, snow (thunder, rain, drought, wet, weather)

Find the three-letter word which can be added to the letters in capitals to make a new word. The new word will complete the sentence sensibly.

**Example** The cat sprang onto the MO. USE

16 What shall we do to CELEBE your birthday? ______

17 I must stop CHEG my pencil. ______

18 The picture was very COLFUL. ______

19 My parents can both ATD Sports Day. ______

20 It's hard to BRHE whilst swimming under water. ______

Fill in the crosswords so that all the given words are included. You have been given one letter as a clue in each crossword. B 19

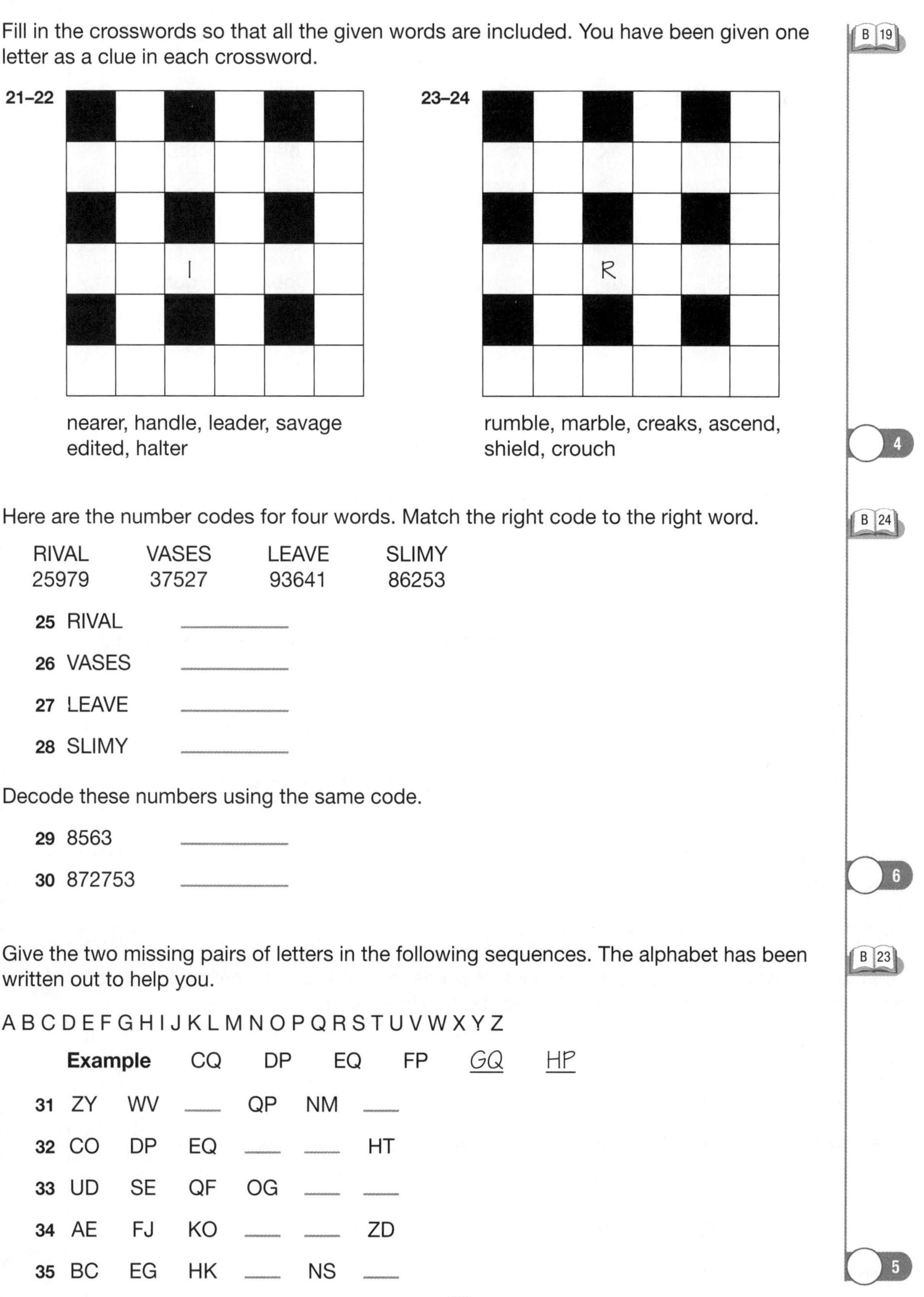

21–22

nearer, handle, leader, savage
edited, halter

23–24

rumble, marble, creaks, ascend,
shield, crouch

4

Here are the number codes for four words. Match the right code to the right word. B 24

| RIVAL | VASES | LEAVE | SLIMY |
|---|---|---|---|
| 25979 | 37527 | 93641 | 86253 |

**25** RIVAL ________

**26** VASES ________

**27** LEAVE ________

**28** SLIMY ________

Decode these numbers using the same code.

**29** 8563 ________

**30** 872753 ________

6

Give the two missing pairs of letters in the following sequences. The alphabet has been written out to help you. B 23

A B C D E F G H I J K L M N O P Q R S T U V W X Y Z

**Example** CQ DP EQ FP *GQ* *HP*

**31** ZY WV ___ QP NM ___

**32** CO DP EQ ___ ___ HT

**33** UD SE QF OG ___ ___

**34** AE FJ KO ___ ___ ZD

**35** BC EG HK ___ NS ___

5

Underline the one word which **cannot be made** from the letters of the word in capital letters.

| | | | | | | |
|---|---|---|---|---|---|---|
| **Example** | STATIONERY | stone | tyres | ration | <u>nation</u> | noisy |
| **36** | BREAKABLE | bleak | area | leer | bleed | rabble |
| **37** | POTATOES | state | tests | soap | taste | post |
| **38** | CONTROVERSY | strove | sorry | overstay | very | store |
| **39** | BELONGINGS | singe | longing | ginger | lobes | gongs |
| **40** | DREADFUL | fared | leader | flared | deaf | ladder |

Complete the following sentences by selecting the most sensible word from each group of words given in the brackets. Underline the words selected.

**Example** The (<u>children</u>, books, foxes) carried the (houses, <u>books</u>, steps) home from the (greengrocer, <u>library</u>, factory).

**41** The cake was (burnt, frozen, ready) because she was too late removing it from the (cupboard, oven, shop).

**42** (Happy, Energetic, Tired) children who don't get enough (food, sleep, drink) find it hard to concentrate at (home, play, school).

**43** The (hamster, dog, horse) stayed in the (kennel, nest, den) while it was (windy, raining, playing) outside.

**44** Read the (question, reply, word), then carefully (imagine, guess, plan) your (answer, problem, subject).

**45** Everyone was (sad, pleased, hurt) that we had a great (holiday, birthday, marriage) that (night, season, summer).

Find the letter which will complete both pairs of words, ending the first word and starting the second. The same letter must be used for both pairs of words.

**Example** mea (<u>t</u>) able fi (<u>t</u>) ub

**46** bar (__) ettle wal (__) now

**47** bea (__) est gri (__) ose

**48** fac (__) ase sal (__) ast

**49** ro (__) old com (__) lack

**50** for (__) ask war (__) ent

Look at the first group of three words. The word in the middle has been made from the other two words. Complete the second group of three words in the same way, making a new word in the middle. B 18

| | | | | | | |
|---|---|---|---|---|---|---|
| **Example** | PAIN | INTO | TOOK | ALSO | SOON | ONLY |
| **51** | BOWL | BORE | READ | HARD | ________ | VEST |
| **52** | HINT | THAW | WEAK | OPEN | ________ | EASY |
| **53** | TIED | DONE | FRONT | LIMP | ________ | STALE |
| **54** | BALL | WELL | WEIRD | LEAN | ________ | MOIST |
| **55** | PRAYS | CHAP | PATCH | ROAST | ________ | WRIST |

5

DESIRE DESCRIBE DESPAIR DESERVE DESCEND B 20

If these words were placed in alphabetical order, which one would come:

**56** fourth? ________

**57** first? ________

**58** second? ________

3

A B C D and E are five cars in a race. B 25

C finishes three minutes ahead of E.

D takes fifteen minutes to complete the race, which is three minutes slower than E.

A wins the race, beating C by two minutes and B by four minutes.

**59** Which car comes last? ________

**60** How many minutes does C take to complete the race? ________

2

If s = 1, t = 2, u = 3, v = 4, w = 5 and x = 6, find the value of the following. B 26

**61** $(t \times u) + s =$ ________

**62** $\frac{x}{u} =$ ________

**63** $(w \times v) \div t =$ ________

**64** $u \times u =$ ________

4

Read the first two statements and then underline one of the four options below that must be true. B 25

**65** 'Gold is a metal. Rings can be made of gold.'

Rings are always made of metal.

Rings are usually made of gold.

Rings can be made of metal.

Gold is an expensive metal.

1

Underline the pair of words most opposite in meaning. B 9

| | | | |
|---|---|---|---|
| **Example** | cup, mug | coffee, milk | hot, cold |
| **66** | vague, certain | coarse, rough | modern, new |
| **67** | fall, drop | purchase, buy | scatter, collect |
| **68** | satisfy, disappoint | scare, panic | promise, pledge |
| **69** | provide, supply | undermine, enhance | advice, recommendation |
| **70** | bronze, copper | nervous, stressed | unusual, ordinary |

5

Underline two words, one from each group, that go together to form a new word. The word in the first group always comes first. B 8

| | | |
|---|---|---|
| **Example** | (hand, green, for) | (light, house, sure) |
| **71** | (out, in, wide) | (light, sect, part) |
| **72** | (through, in, though) | (sign, full, out) |
| **73** | (what, we, no) | (mad, lie, at) |
| **74** | (all, at, in) | (track, together, tempt) |
| **75** | (act, be, leg) | (for, am, all) |

5

A B C D E F G H I J K L M N O P Q R S T U V W X Y Z

Solve the problems by working out the letter codes. B 24

**76** If the code for JURY is HSPW, what is the code for CORAL? ________

**77** If the code for SHARP is UJCTR, what is the code for ALIBI? ________

**78** If the code for PLANK is LHWJG, what does the code NECDP mean? ________

**79** If the code for MINCE is NKQGJ, what is the code for HARBOUR? ________

**80** If the code for FOUR is GNVQ, what is the code for ARCH? ________

5

***Now go to the Progress Chart to record your score!*** **Total** 80

# Paper 9

Underline the two words on each line which are made from the same letters. B 7

| | | | | | | |
|---|---|---|---|---|---|---|
| **Example** | TAP | PET | TEA | POT | EAT | |
| **1** | METEOR | LAMENT | TREMOR | METAL | MENTAL | LATER |
| **2** | START | TASTE | STATE | PLEAT | TRAPS | TRUST |
| **3** | REWARD | FREE | DRAFT | DRAWER | REFER | WAFER |
| **4** | TRACT | CHEAT | CRATE | ACHE | REACT | RATE |
| **5** | STOAT | OATS | STORE | TOES | ROSE | TOAST |

5

Underline the word in the brackets closest in meaning to the word in capitals. B 5

**Example** UNHAPPY (unkind death laughter <u>sad</u> friendly)

6 QUANTITY (ingredients long cooking order amount)

7 RAMBLE (hiker stroll trail thorn path)

8 AWKWARD (graceful simple skilful false difficult)

9 GRAZE (knee fall scrape plaster skin)

10 FLAIR (secret lie truth talent whisper) 5

A B C D E F G H I J K L M N O P Q R S T U V W X Y Z

If Z M R R M K is the code for BOTTOM, what do these codes stand for? B 24

11 R M K Z ______

12 E P M S L B ______

13 E Y P B C L ______

What are the codes for the following words?

14 EARTH ______

15 LOWEST ______ 5

Find the four-letter word hidden at the end of one word and the beginning of the next word. The order of the letters may not be changed. B 21

**Example** The children had bats and balls. *sand*

16 The team did not win a single match this year. ______

17 I hope I can have a brand new phone for my birthday. ______

18 I do hope eleven pounds isn't too much to spend. ______

19 She always helps out when needed. ______

20 Money is also urgently needed by the charity. ______ 5

Underline the two words, one from each group, which are the most opposite in meaning. B 9

**Example** (dawn, <u>early</u>, awake) (<u>late</u>, stop, sunrise)

21 (open, shut, near) (closed, almost, stop)

22 (trip, war, down) (battle, fall, peace)

23 (alert, bright, perfect) (awake, distracted, clever)

24 (deliberate, aim, hostile) (accidental, unfriendly, planned)

25 (secret, essential, locate) (discover, find, unimportant)

26 (flee, weekend, busy) (remain, walk, wander)

27 (happy, mad, complete) (sane, whole, joyful) 7

Read the first two statements and then underline one of the four options below that must be true. B 25

**28** 'Many mammals are plant-eaters. Some mammals live in Africa.'

Some mammals live in herds.
Many plants are found only in Africa.
Some animals in Africa feed on leaves.
Most of the animals in Africa are mammals.

Read the first two statements and then underline one of the four options below that must be true.

**29** 'Language is based on words. Letters are used for each sound in a word.'

Words are usually written.
Sounds can be represented by letters.
There are many different languages.
All languages use the same alphabet.

2

Fill in the crosswords so that all the given words are included. You have been given one letter as a clue in each crossword. B 19

**30–31**

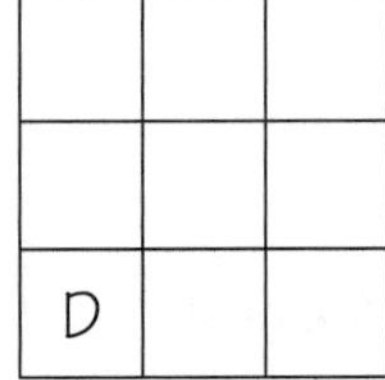

lap, pot, ego, dot, led, ago

**32–33**

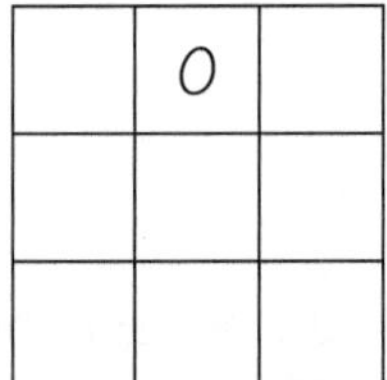

two, oar, eye, way, ore, toe

**34–35**

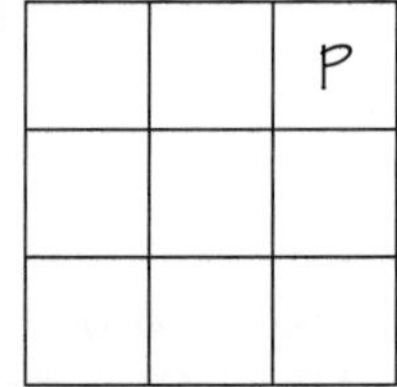

dam, ice, pet, ace, met, dip

6

Give the two missing numbers in the following sequences. B 23

| | | | | | | | |
|---|---|---|---|---|---|---|---|
| **Example** | 2 | 4 | 6 | 8 | 10 | 12 | |
| **36** | 3 | ___ | 9 | 12 | ___ | 18 | 21 |
| **37** | 7 | 9 | 13 | 19 | ___ | ___ | 49 |
| **38** | ___ | 42 | 31 | 22 | ___ | 10 | 7 |
| **39** | 6 | ___ | ___ | 30 | 38 | 46 | 54 |
| **40** | 14 | 36 | 21 | 30 | ___ | ___ | 35 |

5

Find two letters which will end the first word and start the second word. B 10

**Example** rea (c h) air

**41** cha (___ ___) vade
**42** cau (___ ___) rious
**43** norm (___ ___) ways
**44** rememb (___ ___) ror
**45** toa (___ ___) reet

5

Underline the two words which are the odd ones out in the following groups of words. B 4

| | | | | | |
|---|---|---|---|---|---|
| **Example** | black | king | purple | green | house |
| **46** | metre | litre | centimetre | kilometre | kilogram |
| **47** | shout | look | whisper | march | talk |
| **48** | dull | clear | boring | unexciting | weather |
| **49** | London | city | country | France | town |
| **50** | promote | encourage | hinder | boost | depress |

5

Underline the one word in the brackets which will go equally well with both the pairs of words outside the brackets. B 5

| | | | |
|---|---|---|---|
| **Example** | rush, attack | cost, fee | (price, hasten, strike, charge, money) |
| **51** stone, pebble | sway, wobble | | (danger, rock, roll, hard, rough) |
| **52** irritable, cross | brisk, lively | | (touchy, sluggish, quick, snappy, hasty) |
| **53** idea, knowledge | agreement, pact | | (intelligence, understanding, cooperation, patient, acceptance) |
| **54** division, group | grade, course | | (collection, student, class, teacher, sort) |
| **55** bud, flower | grow, progress | | (plant, increase, movement, stem, blossom) |

5

Change the first word of the third pair in the same way as the other pairs to give a new word. B 18

| | | | |
|---|---|---|---|
| **Example** | bind, hind | bare, hare | but, hut |
| **56** | bit, bite | kit, kite | sit, ________ |
| **57** | chill, hill | shops, hops | cover, ________ |
| **58** | deed, feed | dish, fish | date, ________ |
| **59** | file, life | dire, ride, | rise, ________ |
| **60** | moth, hot | with, hit | mash, ________ |

5

Rearrange the letters in capitals to make another word. The new word has something to do with the first two words. B 16

| | | | | |
|---|---|---|---|---|
| **Example** | spot | soil | SAINT | STAIN |
| **61** | dull | dim | DEAF | ________ |
| **62** | genuine | true | EARL | ________ |
| **63** | short | quick | FIBRE | ________ |
| **64** | violent | fury | GEAR | ________ |
| **65** | mistake | oversight | SEPAL | ________ |

5

Complete the following sentences by selecting the most sensible word from each group of words given in the brackets. Underline the words selected. B 14

**Example** The (children, books, foxes) carried the (houses, books, steps) home from the (greengrocer, library, factory).

66 We will (go, leave, listen) to the (cinema, holiday, moon) next (evening, week, day).

67 As (autumn, spring, winter) came the (leaves, petals, branches) began to (grow, develop, fall) from the trees.

68 You can take some (friends, money, clothes) to (play, spend, wear) with in the (bank, park, bath).

69 My (pets, parents, toys) go to bed after (watching, playing, counting) the (road, books, television).

70 A (clock, thermometer, radio) measures (temperature, time, sound) to the nearest (week, wave, second). 5

Here are the number codes for four words. Match the right code to the right word. B 24

| PEAR | AREA | SOAP | ROPE |
|---|---|---|---|
| 7254 | 6243 | 4356 | 5635 |

71 PEAR ________

72 AREA ________

73 SOAP ________

74 ROPE ________

75 Write POSE in code. ________ 5

Change one word so that the sentence makes sense. Underline the word you are taking out and write your new word on the line. B 14

**Example** I waited in line to buy a book to see the film. ticket

76 As it's Saturday tomorrow, you can get up late to watch the film. ________

77 She spent her pocket money because she couldn't find anything tempting to buy. ________

78 Brush your hair after eating so many sweets. ________

79 Our cinema doesn't always show the most recent songs. ________

80 She took a sip of her drink because she was hungry. ________ 5

***Now go to the Progress Chart to record your score!*** **Total** 80

# Paper 10

Give the two missing pairs of letters in the following sequences. The alphabet has been written out to help you. B 23

A B C D E F G H I J K L M N O P Q R S T U V W X Y Z

| | | | | | | |
|---|---|---|---|---|---|---|
| **Example** | CQ | DP | EQ | FP | GQ | HP |
| **1** | JD | KE | LF | MG | ___ | ___ |
| **2** | AJ | BI | DG | GD | ___ | ___ |
| **3** | UB | PB | LD | ___ | GF | ___ |
| **4** | HT | GU | ___ | EW | DX | ___ |
| **5** | GV | HU | JS | KR | ___ | ___ |

5

Choose two words, one from each set of brackets, to complete the sentences in the best way. B 15

**Example** Smile is to happiness as (drink, tear, shout) is to (whisper, laugh, sorrow).

**6** Uncle is to aunt as (husband, son, father) is to (grandmother, relative, wife).

**7** Reveal is to show as (unite, copy, glance) is to (write, join, divide).

**8** Lion is to den as (mouse, pig, bee) is to (stable, sty, sting).

**9** Sad is to melancholy as (ghostly, spirited, lazy) is to (vigorous, calm, spiteful).

**10** Depart is to arrive as (deny, agree, accept) is to (state, respond, admit). 5

Find the three-letter word which can be added to the letters in capitals to make a new word. The new word will complete the sentence sensibly. B 22

**Example** The cat sprang onto the MO. USE

**11** You can ARGE to have a friend to play next week. ________

**12** She felt LLY once the other children had gone home. ________

**13** The answer was explained CLLY. ________

**14** Mum, Danika keeps RETING what I say! ________

**15** The Halloween MS scared the younger children. ________ 5

If $a = 6$, $b = 2$, $c = 0$, $d = 5$, $e = 10$, find the answer to these calculations. B 26

**16** $a + d + e =$ ___

**17** $(be) \div d =$ ___

**18** $(a \times b) + d =$ ___

**19** $abc =$ ___

**20** $(d \times e) \div (b \times d) =$ ___ 5

Which one letter can be added to the front of all of these words to make new words? B 12

**Example** care cat crate call

| | | | | | |
|---|---|---|---|---|---|
| 21 | __eek | __ick | __core | __elf | __ack |
| 22 | __oyal | __ure | __uck | __ist | __oad |
| 23 | __ook | __oot | __orn | __our | __ost |
| 24 | __ire | __ice | __eed | __eal | __ale |
| 25 | __oad | __ool | __ent | __ank | __uck |

5

Underline one word in the brackets which is most opposite in meaning to the word in capitals. B 6

**Example** WIDE (broad vague long narrow motorway)

26 HOST (party hostess invite guest speak)

27 ENDLESS (close beginning limited boundary outcome)

28 CATCH (game grab try drop problem)

29 OBJECT (article focus purpose approve plan)

30 ARTIFICIAL (false reliable fake genuine environment)

5

Rearrange the muddled letters in capitals to make a proper word. The answer will complete the sentence sensibly. B 16

**Example** A BEZAR is an animal with stripes. ZEBRA

31 Put a ATPMS on that before you post it! ________

32 His mother was ODUPR of his achievements. ________

33 I have ITENIVD everyone to my party. ________

34 The witness described the DICTENAC. ________

35 I lost my SERPU outside the bank. ________

5

Fill in the crosswords so that all the given words are included. You have been given one letter as a clue in each crossword. B 19

36–37

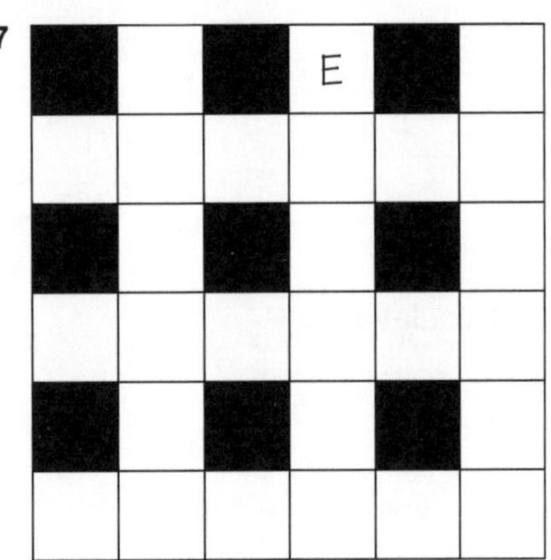


stodgy, matted, storey, editor, impart, amidst

38–39

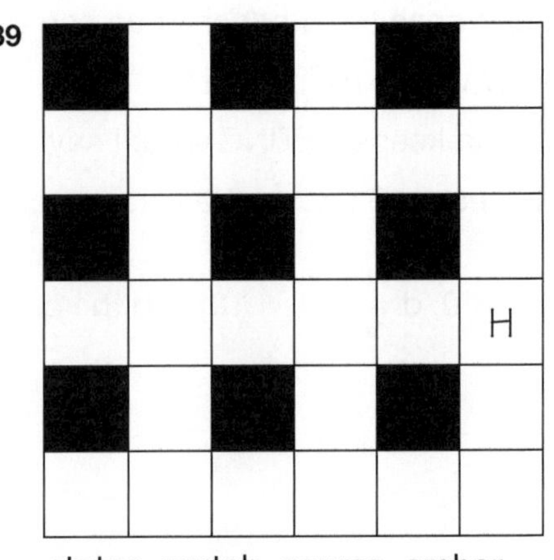


states, crutch, course, archer, censor, loiter

4

Read the first two statements and then underline one of the four options below that must be true. B 25

40 'Tea is grown in China. Many people drink tea.'

Most people in China grow tea plants.

Tea is a more popular drink than coffee.

Some people drink Chinese tea.

Tea is a hot drink. 1

Here are the number codes for four words. Match the right code to the right word. B 24

| EAST | TEAM | LIKE | SULK |
|---|---|---|---|
| 6924 | 1537 | 5361 | 2845 |

41 EAST ________

42 TEAM ________

43 LIKE ________

44 SULK ________

45 Write MILK in code. ________

46 Decode 6531. ________ 6

Poppy's birthday is in the month which ends with the 20th letter of the alphabet. Her brother's birthday is eight months later. B 25

47 In which month is Poppy's brother's birthday? ________ 1

Underline the one word which **can be made** from the letters of the word in capital letters. B 7

| | | | | | | |
|---|---|---|---|---|---|---|
| **Example** | CHAMPION | camping | notch | peach | cramp | chimp |
| 48 | CAULIFLOWER | lions | fault | relay | colder | crawl |
| 49 | FLAVOURING | reign | vowel | gravel | grain | float |
| 50 | STRAINED | timed | darts | stripe | earl | nested |

3

Look at the first group of three words. The word in the middle has been made from the other two words. Complete the second group of three words in the same way, making a new word in the middle. B 18

| | | | | | | |
|---|---|---|---|---|---|---|
| **Example** | PAIN | INTO | TOOK | ALSO | SOON | ONLY |
| 51 | LEND | DONE | ALSO | SPAT | ________ | FOUR |
| 52 | ROSE | LOSE | SOUL | MILK | ________ | SOAR |
| 53 | KIND | DICE | LACE | WASP | ________ | MIST |
| 54 | PEAK | PEAT | MEAT | WAIT | ________ | HIVE |
| 55 | WROTE | LOWER | RELAY | VEINS | ________ | LARCH |

5

Add one letter to the word in capital letters to make a new word. The meaning of the new word is given in the clue. B 12

**Example** PLAN simple plain

56 HARE split, divide ________

57 TRUST drive, force ________

58 VICE human sound ________

59 CLAN washed ________

60 SIFT rapid ________ 5

Fill in the missing letters. The alphabet has been written out to help you. B 23

A B C D E F G H I J K L M N O P Q R S T U V W X Y Z

**Example** AB is to CD as PQ is to RS.

61 CF is to EH as RU is to ____.

62 VX is to UY as DG is to ____.

63 TW is to VZ as LP is to ____.

64 JK is to HI as ST is to ____.

65 SW is to VU as OG is to ____. 5

Underline the two words, one from each group, which are closest in meaning. B 3

**Example** (race, shop, start) (finish, begin, end)

66 (justify, question, right) (legal, explain, penalty)

67 (rare, common, unusual) (sense, real, ordinary)

68 (tap, liquid, flood) (drought, overflow, trickle)

69 (stale, processed, cooked) (raw, old, fresh)

70 (mess, lose, wreck) (destroy, ship, save) 5

Move one letter from the first word and add it to the second word to make two new words. B 13

**Example** hunt sip hut snip

71 fable lie ________ ________

72 port fail ________ ________

73 stable rush ________ ________

74 craft up ________ ________

75 grain net ________ ________ 5

Write these words in alphabetical order. B 20

| | | | | | |
|---|---|---|---|---|---|
| 76 | artificial | artistic | artful | arrogant | arrest |
| 77 | expand | exhilarate | expectancy | exile | exhibit |
| 78 | recite | rebel | reason | reassure | rebuild |
| 79 | illusion | illegible | illogical | illicit | illustrate |
| 80 | foreign | forcible | forever | forecast | force |

5

**Now go to the Progress Chart to record your score!** Total 80

# Paper 11

Change the first word into the last word by changing one letter at a time and making two new, different words in the middle. B 13

| | | | | |
|---|---|---|---|---|
| **Example** | TEAK | <u>TEAT</u> | <u>TENT</u> | RENT |
| 1 | FIRE | ______ | ______ | FALL |
| 2 | FISH | ______ | ______ | MUST |
| 3 | NEAR | ______ | ______ | SELL |
| 4 | KERB | ______ | ______ | HARD |
| 5 | LACE | ______ | ______ | VILE |
| 6 | RICE | ______ | ______ | FACT |

6

Complete the following sentences by selecting the most sensible word from each group of words given in the brackets. Underline the words selected. B 14

**Example** The (<u>children</u>, books, foxes) carried the (houses, <u>books</u>, steps) home from the (greengrocer, <u>library</u>, factory).

7 It's important to make sure that your (customer, visitor, pet) doesn't (drink, eat, work) too much and become (lazy, overweight, bossy).

8 People who (travel, shop, listen) through space in a (computer, TV, rocket) are called (hikers, astronauts, dreamers).

9 Tom's (friend, teacher, mother) wrote in his (card, invitation, report) that he must (learn, improve, spell) his handwriting.

10 Most of her birthday (presents, cake, cards) showed pictures of (cats, candles, toys), but her favourite animal is actually a (doll, dog, drawing).

4

Find a word that can be put in front of each of the following words to make new, compound words.

| | | | | | |
|---|---|---|---|---|---|
| **Example** | cast | fall | ward | pour | down |
| **11** pad | book | paper | worthy | | _______ |
| **12** come | cast | all | grown | | _______ |
| **13** back | bulb | card | light | | _______ |
| **14** room | robe | tub | water | | _______ |
| **15** standing | line | ground | foot | | _______ |

Find a word that is similar in meaning to the word in capital letters and that rhymes with the second word.

| | | |
|---|---|---|
| **Example** CABLE | tyre | wire |
| **16** SWINDLE | beat | _______ |
| **17** STORY | sail | _______ |
| **18** PAINFUL | moor | _______ |
| **19** ARROW | heart | _______ |
| **20** MATCHED | cared | _______ |

Change the first word of the third pair in the same way as the other pairs to give a new word.

| | | |
|---|---|---|
| **Example** bind, hind | bare, hare | but, hut |
| **21** tall, tail | fall, fail | wall, _______ |
| **22** risk, skin | wish, shin | bath, _______ |
| **23** net, nest | pet, pest | bet, _______ |
| **24** gape, page | dame, made | tame, _______ |
| **25** mare, ream | name, mean | post, _______ |

Complete the following expressions by underlining the missing word.

**Example** Frog is to tadpole as swan is to (duckling, baby, cygnet).

**26** Wrist is to arm as ankle is to (foot, leg, toe).

**27** Pleased is to delighted as solemn is to (tired, frightened, serious).

**28** Sour is to sugary as reasonable is to (sensible, outrageous, thoughtful).

**29** Fee is to cost as margin is to (paper, book, edge).

**30** Clamour is to silence as readily is to (promptly, reluctantly, actually).

Fill in the crosswords so that all the given words are included. You have been given one letter as a clue in each crossword. B 19

**31–32**

| ■ | | ■ | | ■ | |
|---|---|---|---|---|---|
| | | | | | E |
| ■ | | ■ | | ■ | |
| | | | | | |
| ■ | | ■ | | ■ | |
| | | | | | |

upside, meddle, spread,
riddle, advert, repeat.

**33–34**

| ■ | | ■ | | ■ | |
|---|---|---|---|---|---|
| | | | | | |
| ■ | | ■ | | ■ | |
| | | | | | |
| ■ | | ■ | | ■ | |
| | | P | | | |

staple, stains, appear,
neatly, digest, osprey.

4

Here are the number codes for four words. Match the right code to the right word. B 24

| ECHO | COAL | HALO | LACE |
|---|---|---|---|
| 4216 | 6145 | 3162 | 5432 |

**35** ECHO ________

**36** COAL ________

**37** HALO ________

**38** LACE ________

**39** Write ACHE in code. ________

**40** Write HOLE in code. ________

6

Give the two missing pairs of letters or numbers in the following sequences. The alphabet has been written out to help you with questions 41, 42 and 43. B 23

A B C D E F G H I J K L M N O P Q R S T U V W X Y Z

| | | | | | | |
|---|---|---|---|---|---|---|
| **Example** | CQ | DP | EQ | FP | <u>GQ</u> | <u>HP</u> |
| **41** | RD | ___ | TF | UG | VH | ___ |
| **42** | CO | EM | GK | ___ | KG | ___ |
| **43** | AV | BU | CT | ___ | ___ | FQ |
| **44** | 25 | 28 | ___ | 34 | 37 | ___ |
| **45** | 52 | 57 | 54 | 59 | ___ | ___ |

5

Underline the pair of words most similar in meaning. B 5

**Example** come, go roam, wander fear, fare

46 attach, unfasten near, distant negotiate, discuss

47 waited, walked support, assist rapidly, slowly

48 peace, calm help, ignore cost, purse

49 graceful, clumsy gradual, immediate determined, persistent 4

Read the first two statements and then underline one of the four options below that must be true. B 25

50 'Kumiko often goes to French Club on Saturday morning. Yesterday was Thursday.'

Kumiko enjoys learning French.

Kumiko is going to French Club today.

Tomorrow is Saturday.

French Club lasts for two hours. 1

Find two letters which will end the first word and start the second word. B 10

**Example** rea (c h) air

51 ma (__ __) elf

52 dra (__ __) nage

53 enou (__ __) ost

54 priva (__ __) lephone

55 plea (__ __) cond 5

Underline the one word in the brackets which will go equally well with both the pairs of words outside the brackets. B 5

**Example** rush, attack cost, fee (price, hasten, strike, charge, money)

56 transport, aviation exit, fleeing (soaring, escape, trip, flight, aeroplane)

57 slim, slender prune, crop (neat, trim, compact, tidy, smart)

58 advert, flyer observe, see (paper, notice, look, read, say)

59 tie, stalemate trace, sketch (raffle, trace, skill, draw, prize)

60 express, show ventilate, freshen (appear, disclose, space, air, expose) 5

Underline the two words which are the odd ones out in the following groups of words. B 4

| | | | | | |
|---|---|---|---|---|---|
| **Example** | black | <u>king</u> | purple | green | <u>house</u> |
| **61** | disease | fever | nurse | infection | medicine |
| **62** | curiosity | involvement | boredom | concern | indifference |
| **63** | coffee | glass | cider | cup | milk |
| **64** | eat | chew | hunger | starving | munch |
| **65** | wings | robin | beak | ostrich | talon |

5

Find the four-letter word which can be added to the letters in capitals to make a new word. The new word will complete the sentence sensibly. B 22

**Example** They enjoyed the BCAST. ROAD

**66** The bird was kept busy SEING for food and protecting the nest. ________

**67** The truck BED the road so no one could pass. ________

**68** He watched a very INTEING programme about dinosaurs. ________

**69** I REED the book to the library on time. ________

**70** It is IMANT to protect your skin when the sun is strong. ________

5

Remove one letter from the word in capital letters to leave a new word. The meaning of the new word is given in the clue. B 12

| | | | |
|---|---|---|---|
| **Example** | AUNT | an insect | ant |
| **71** | PAINTING | breathless | ________ |
| **72** | PASTRY | small pie | ________ |
| **73** | SPORT | harbour | ________ |
| **74** | SLIGHT | glimpse | ________ |
| **75** | QUIET | give up | ________ |

5

Underline the two words which are made from the same letters. B 7

| | | | | | | |
|---|---|---|---|---|---|---|
| **Example** | TAP | PET | <u>TEA</u> | POT | <u>EAT</u> | |
| **76** | REPEAT | TRAPPED | DEPART | TAPER | PARTED | DRAPE |
| **77** | DIME | MERIT | TIMED | METRE | REMIT | TREMOR |
| **78** | SEVER | SIEVE | SEVEN | VERSE | VEINS | NEVER |
| **79** | RETRACT | TRACER | RETRACE | CATERER | TRACTOR | REACT |
| **80** | HOSES | SHORT | HORSE | HORNS | SHOTS | SHORE |

5

*Now go to the Progress Chart to record your score!* Total 80

# Paper 12

Find the letter which will complete both pairs of words, ending the first word and starting the second. The same letter must be used for both pairs of words. B 10

**Example** mea (t) able fit (t) ub

1 batc (___) eap pitc (___) eave

2 dee (___) amp fon (___) eter

3 mal (___) ask fac (___) usk

4 clu (___) lunt cra (___) rim

5 eve (___) eon wea (___) oble

6 stai (___) oam flou (___) ent 6

Spell the following words backwards. Write numbers underneath the words to indicate their new alphabetical order. B 20

| | | | |
|---|---|---|---|
| 7 INVISIBLE | IMPOSSIBLE | INEDIBLE | BUBBLE |
| ______ | ______ | ______ | ______ |
| 8 JUICE | BRUISE | CRUISE | NUISANCE |
| ______ | ______ | ______ | ______ |
| 9 HOPING | MAKING | WAKING | DRIVING |
| ______ | ______ | ______ | ______ |

3

Five friends, A, B, C, D and E are in a queue to buy tickets at the cinema. B 25

A is not at the back of the queue and has one person in front of him.

E has three people ahead of him, and is standing in front of D.

B is at the front of the queue.

10 Which person is in the middle of the queue? ______ 1

A B C D E F G H I J K L M N O P Q R S T U V W X Y Z

If A = 1, B = 2, C = 3 and so on, find the value of the following words by adding the letters together. B 26

11 CAB ______

12 CAGE ______

13 BED ______ 3

Fill in the crosswords so that all the given words are included. You have been given one letter as a clue in each crossword. B 19

**14–15**

| | | |
|---|---|---|
| | | W |
| | | |
| | | |

wet, ewe, dog,
get, owe, dew

**16–17**

| | | |
|---|---|---|
| | | |
| | | |
| E | | |

era, urn, mad,
see, end, sum

4

A B C D E F G H I J K L M N O P Q R S T U V W X Y Z

If the code for COUNT is XLFMG, what are the codes for these words? B 24

**18** COT ________

**19** NEAT ________

**20** FISH ________

3

Underline the two words, one from each group, which are the most opposite in meaning. B 9

**Example** (dawn, <u>early</u>, wake) (<u>late</u>, stop, sunrise)

**21** (light, appear, view) (scenery, glow, vanish)

**22** (type, sort, variety) (assortment, routine, different)

**23** (ready, easily, gladly) (eager, unprepared, willingly)

**24** (fee, jewel, treasured) (rich, ignored, cheap)

4

Read the first two statements and then underline one of the four options below that must be true. B 25

**25** 'Most dogs wear a collar. Some collars have a name tag.'

All pets wear name tags.

Some dogs without collars might get lost.

Not all dogs have name tags.

Name tags are sold in pet shops.

1

Rearrange the muddled letters in capitals to make a proper word. The answer will complete the sentence sensibly. B 16

**Example** A BEZAR is an animal with stripes. <u>ZEBRA</u>

**26** The waiter will VERSE the coffee. ________

**27** Let us UNTIE our forces. ________

**28** Cameron DENSE to pass his swimming test. ________

**29** Can you DEARTH the cotton through the needle? ________

**30** Turn off the PALM before you go to sleep. ________

5

Complete the following sentences in the best way by choosing one word from each set of brackets.

B 15

**Example** Tall is to (tree, short, colour) as narrow is to (thin, white, wide).

31 First is to (early, number, beginning) as last is to (only, single, ending).

32 Frog is to (croaks, green, pond) as lion is to (cub, roars, kills).

33 Minimum is to (bad, least, maximum) as light is to (weight, heavy, load).

34 Child is to (children, play, school) as woman is to (dress, women, husband).

35 Dishonest is to (false, wrong, trustworthy) as protect is to (barrier, threaten, careful).

Look at the first group of three words. The word in the middle has been made from the other two words. Complete the second group of three words in the same way, making a new word in the middle.

| | | | | | | |
|---|---|---|---|---|---|---|
| **Example** | PAIN | INTO | TOOK | ALSO | SOON | ONLY |
| 36 | PINT | NAIL | PALE | TREE | ______ | TANK |
| 37 | RAMP | ROAM | BOAT | BULL | ______ | COIN |
| 38 | PURE | WIRE | WISP | YAWN | ______ | DOTE |
| 39 | CLOAK | MOLE | MODEL | WEIGH | ______ | THIRD |
| 40 | WEAN | SAFE | SELF | STOP | ______ | LEAF |

Find the four-letter word which can be added to the letters in capitals to make a new word. The new word will complete the sentence sensibly.

**Example** They enjoyed the BCAST. ROAD

41 The wrecked car was AONED in the field. ______

42 Parents will be INED as soon as a decision is made. ______

43 Drive carefully past CYCS. ______

44 REING children for good behaviour is important. ______

45 They played BADON in the garden during the holiday. ______

Underline the two words which are the odd ones out in the following groups of words.

| | | | | | |
|---|---|---|---|---|---|
| **Example** | black | king | purple | green | house |
| 46 | aeroplane | pilot | car | mechanic | engineer |
| 47 | lake | valley | plain | harbour | mountain |
| 48 | begin | suspend | terminate | start | discontinue |
| 49 | spiteful | cruel | compassionate | nasty | charitable |
| 50 | litter | rubbish | herd | insects | swarm |

Change one word so that the sentence makes sense. Underline the word you are taking out and write your new word on the line. B 14

**Example** I waited in line to buy a book to see the film. ticket

51 Writing in a dairy is a good way to remember special occasions. ______

52 When you are playing football, the aim is to score as many hits as possible. ______

53 Do not leave very young adults unsupervised with a dog. ______

54 You can use your dictionary to find out what a sum means. ______

55 A guinea pig is a small animal, often kept as a toy. ______ 5

Add one letter to the word in capital letters to make a new word. The meaning of the new word is given in the clue. B 12

**Example** PLAN simple plain

56 EXIT to be alive ______

57 STOKE pat gently ______

58 VALE worth ______

59 WARY tired ______

60 MINE cut into small pieces ______ 5

Choose two words, one from each set of brackets, to complete the sentences in the best way. B 15

**Example** Smile is to happiness as (drink, tear, shout) is to (whisper, laugh, sorrow).

61 Ideal is to perfect as (genuine, gentle, generous) is to (common, capable, calm).

62 Immense is to enormous as (cold, shivery, chilled) is to (hot, unfriendly, pleasant).

63 Sporty is to athlete as (clumsy, graceful, heavy) is to (plumber, ballerina, chef).

64 Ignore is to notice as (prevent, perform, plunge) is to (allow, check, block). 4

Here are the number codes for three words. Match the right code to the right word. B 24

| DEFY | OBEY | YEAR |
|---|---|---|
| 8342 | 6472 | 2415 |

65 DEFY ______

66 OBEY ______

67 YEAR ______

Decode these numbers using the same code.

68 3862 ______

69 35416 ______ 5

Fill in the missing letters. The alphabet has been written out to help you.

A B C D E F G H I J K L M N O P Q R S T U V W X Y Z

**Example** AB is to CD as PQ is to RS.

70 CXG is to DWH as HNA is to ____.

71 HEQ is to JGS as WRK is to ____.

72 BC is to YX as DE is to ____.

73 JFC is to IEB as OVK is to ____.

74 AD is to ZW as BE is to ____.

B 23

5

Give the two missing pairs of letters or numbers in the following sequences. The alphabet has been written out to help you.

A B C D E F G H I J K L M N O P Q R S T U V W X Y Z

| | | | | | | |
|---|---|---|---|---|---|---|
| **Example** | CQ | DP | EQ | FP | GQ | HP |
| 75 | AC | DF | ___ | JL | MO | ___ |
| 76 | ___ | DV | FT | HR | ___ | LN |
| 77 | VE | ___ | ___ | SH | RI | QJ |
| 78 | 3 | 6 | 12 | 21 | ___ | ___ |
| 79 | 19 | 15 | ___ | 14 | 17 | ___ |
| 80 | 2 | 8 | 14 | 20 | ___ | ___ |

B 23

6

***Now go to the Progress Chart to record your score!*** **Total** 80

# Paper 13

Complete the following sentences in the best way by choosing one word from each set of brackets.

**Example** Tall is to (tree, short, colour) as narrow is to (thin, white, wide).

1 Complicated is to (wicked, tricky, straightforward) as loyal is to (faithful, difficult, awkward).

2 Prize is to (certificate, badge, reward) as penalty is to (punishment, gift, payment).

3 Exclude is to (allow, school, reject) as include is to (refuse, accept, destroy).

4 Bat is to (ball, wing, cricket) as rabbit is to (grass, hop, paw).

5 Imaginary is to (mind, possible, invented) as real is to (actual, copy, fake).

B 15

5

Remove one letter from the word in capital letters to leave a new word. The meaning of the new word is given in the clue.

| | | | |
|---|---|---|---|
| **Example** | AUNT | an insect | ant |
| **6** | BEAN | forbid | ______ |
| **7** | HALVE | possess | ______ |
| **8** | SPLASH | cut | ______ |
| **9** | CARVE | hole under the ground | ______ |
| **10** | PATCH | course of action | ______ |

B 12

5

Underline the two words, one from each group, which are closest in meaning.

| | | |
|---|---|---|
| **Example** | (race, shop, start) | (finish, begin, end) |
| **11** | (behave, reaction, move) | (response, look, knowledge) |
| **12** | (shorten, spread, lessen) | (traffic, expand, carry) |
| **13** | (arrange, definite, fix) | (harm, repair, vary) |
| **14** | (degree, lesser, deliberate) | (college, mistake, amount) |
| **15** | (spot, nest, hole) | (filling, opening, round) |

B 3

5

Give the two missing numbers in the following sequences.

| | | | | | | | |
|---|---|---|---|---|---|---|---|
| **16** | 9 | 7 | 12 | 10 | ___ | ___ | 18 |
| **17** | 22 | ___ | 36 | 43 | 50 | 57 | ___ |
| **18** | 2 | 4 | 4 | ___ | 6 | 12 | ___ |
| **19** | 9 | 16 | 25 | 36 | ___ | ___ | 81 |
| **20** | 10 | 15 | ___ | ___ | 30 | 35 | 40 |

B 23

5

Claire and Amy are studying Science and Maths, and Harry and Fred study History and Geography.
Jacob and Henry like Art and Spanish, but Amelia's worst subject is French.
Ravi does Maths, but no longer has Geography lessons.
All the girls do Drama.

**21** Which children are learning more than two subjects? ______________

B 25

1

A B C D E F G H I J K L M N O P Q R S T U V W X Y Z

Solve the problems by working out the letter codes.

**22** If the code for SOUP is VRXS, what is the code for SAVE? ______

**23** If the code for FOLDER is HMNBGP, what is the code for MISTAKE? ______

**24** If the code for BRAKE is DUEPK, what does the code YLRIE mean? ______

B 24

3

Read the first two statements and then underline one of the four options below that must be true. B 25

25 'Crows and magpies are birds. Birds lay eggs.'

Magpies are black and white.

Crows lay eggs.

Many crows and magpies share nests.

Nests are only used for laying eggs. 1

Find two letters which will end the first word and start the second word.

**Example** rea ( c h ) air

26 almo ( ___ ___ ) art

27 exci ( ___ ___ ) mper

28 fra ( ___ ___ ) lon

29 sha ( ___ ___ ) rmit

30 whisp ( ___ ___ ) upt

Find the missing number by using the two numbers outside the brackets in the same way as the other sets of numbers.

**Example** 2 [8] 4 3 [18] 6 5 [25] 5

31 6 [7] 9 8 [9] 11 10 [___] 13

32 7 [7] 49 9 [6] 54 4 [___] 32

33 12 [17] 22 16 [21] 26 2 [___] 12

34 9 [6] 7 10 [7] 8 12 [___] 10

35 24 [4] 6 36 [3] 12 27 [___] 3

Change the first word of the third pair in the same way as the other pairs to give a new word.

**Example** bind, hind bare, hare but, hut

36 hat, hatch mat, match pat, ________

37 bake, beak lake, leak wake, ________

38 trust, us clamp, am bring, ________

39 base, sea fear, are seat, ________

40 line, link tale, talk bare, ________

Underline the one word in the brackets which will go equally well with both the pairs of words outside the brackets.

B 5

| | | | |
|---|---|---|---|
| **Example** | rush, attack | cost, fee | (price, hasten, strike, <u>charge</u>, money) |
| **41** | final, latest | continue, go on | (remain, last, cease, behind, proceed) |
| **42** | thorn, quill | annoy, pester | (tease, stick, needle, stem, poke) |
| **43** | earth, ground | arrive, come down | (planet, rest, soil, land, run) |
| **44** | explain, say | condition, phase | (report, shape, state, situation, express) |
| **45** | strong, firm | stern, strict | (solid, gentle, kind, healthy, tough) |

5

Move one letter from the first word and add it to the second word to make two new words.

B 13

| | | | | |
|---|---|---|---|---|
| **Example** | hunt | sip | hut | snip |
| **46** | brisk | owl | ______ | ______ |
| **47** | brand | ham | ______ | ______ |
| **48** | flame | came | ______ | ______ |
| **49** | board | raw | ______ | ______ |
| **50** | tone | man | ______ | ______ |

5

Give the two missing pairs of letters in the following sequences. The alphabet has been written out to help you.

B 23

A B C D E F G H I J K L M N O P Q R S T U V W X Y Z

| | | | | | | |
|---|---|---|---|---|---|---|
| **Example** | CQ | DP | EQ | FP | GQ | HP |
| **51** | DX | GU | JR | MO | ___ | ___ |
| **52** | BY | ___ | DW | EV | ___ | GT |
| **53** | WC | UE | VD | TF | ___ | ___ |
| **54** | ___ | OP | QR | ST | ___ | WX |

4

Here are the number codes for four words. Match the right code to the right word.

B 24

| ROAD | REAL | DARE | OVER |
|---|---|---|---|
| 5736 | 2463 | 6341 | 6542 |

**55** REAL ______

**56** ROAD ______

**57** DARE ______

**58** OVER ______

Decode these numbers using the same code.

**59** 56236 ______

**60** 26573 ______

6

Look at the first group of three words. The word in the middle has been made from the other two words. Complete the second group of three words in the same way, making a new word in the middle. B 18

| | | | | | | |
|---|---|---|---|---|---|---|
| **Example** | PA<u>IN</u> | INTO | <u>TO</u>OK | ALSO | <u>SOON</u> | ONLY |
| 61 | ARMY | RACE | CHEW | OPEN | ______ | SITS |
| 62 | SLAP | PALM | HELM | REEF | ______ | BARN |
| 63 | CHIRP | RICE | PRICE | ELDER | ______ | DIVER |
| 64 | REIN | NOTE | OTTER | REAP | ______ | INCH |
| 65 | GAME | ROAM | BORE | OVEN | ______ | FAST |

5

Rearrange the letters in capitals to make another word. The new word has something to do with the first two words. B 16

| | | | | |
|---|---|---|---|---|
| **Example** | spot | soil | SAINT | <u>STAIN</u> |
| 66 | unkind | nasty | NAME | ______ |
| 67 | players | game | MEAT | ______ |
| 68 | brave | challenge | READ | ______ |
| 69 | celebrity | twinkling light | RATS | ______ |
| 70 | vibrate | thump | BROTH | ______ |

5

Fill in the crosswords so that all the given words are included. You have been given one letter as a clue in each crossword. B 19

**71–72**

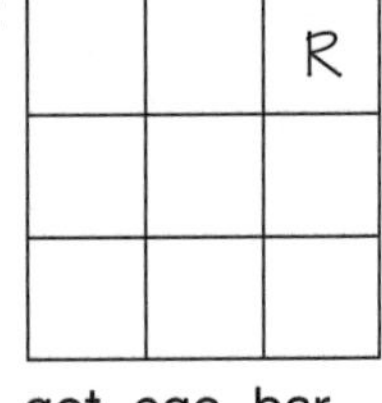

got, ego, bar, ago, rot, beg

**73–74**

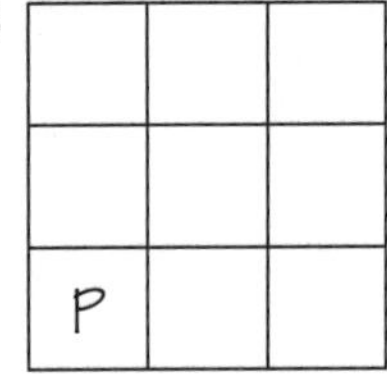

ace, net, tap, ice, pet, tin

4

Choose two words, one from each set of brackets, to complete the sentences in the best way. B 15

**Example** Smile is to happiness as (drink, <u>tear</u>, shout) is to (whisper, laugh, <u>sorrow</u>).

75 Bee is to buzz as (pig, wolf, duck) is to (piglet, lake, howl).

76 Rear is to back as (grab, give, punch) is to (hold, snatch, kick).

77 Crude is to polite as (pile, crowded, sandy) is to (crushed, demolished, deserted).

78 Leaf is to leaves as (cup, eyesight, glass) is to (water, glasses, mugs).

79 Tease is to irritate as (damage, assist, know) is to (harm, ignore, repair).

80 Star is to sky as (sail, wave, greeting) is to (friendly, land, sea).

6

***Now go to the Progress Chart to record your score!*** **Total** 80

## Progress Chart Verbal Reasoning 10–11⁺ years Book 2

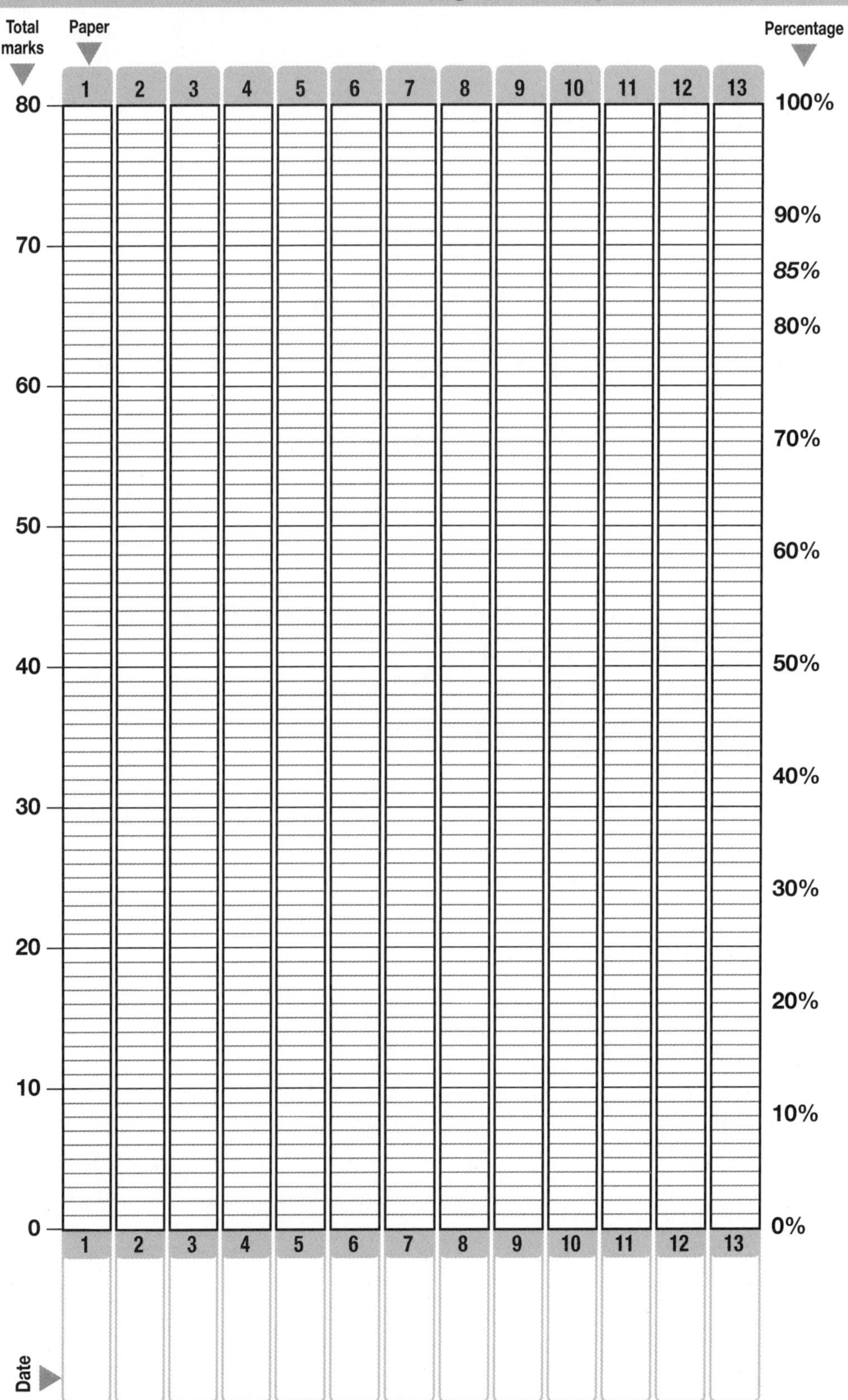


*When you've finished the book use the Next Steps Planner*